⟨ BUDGET-FRIENDLY ⟩
DIABETIC
COOKBOOK
FOR BEGINNERS

**Low-Carb, Quick & Tasty Recipes to Master
Pre-Diabetes, Type 1 & 2 Diabetes with Ease.
Includes 4-Week Smart Meal Plan with
Affordable Ingredients**

ROSY LUKE

GET YOUR
EXTRA CONTENT
NOW!

To download the digital version of these bonuses
you don't need to enter any details except
your name and email address.

EXTRA#1
Blood Sugar Log Book

EXTRA#2
Food Journal Log Book

EXTRA#3
Medication Log Book

EXTRA#4
Recipe Remix: Adapting
Favorites for Diabetic Health

EXTRA#5
Dine Out Smart: A Diabetic's
Guide to Eating Out

SIMPLY SCAN
THE QR CODE BELOW
OR GO TO

bonusbooklovers.com/rosy-luke-bd

SCAN
ME
NOW

Table of Contents

CHAPTER 1: INTRODUCTION

Diabetes is a chronic disease that affects millions of individuals globally. It is distinguished by high blood glucose levels, which occur as a result of the body's failure to make insulin (Type 1) or its inability to efficiently utilize insulin (Type 2).

Diabetes management is critical for overall health and preventing complications. Adhering to a healthy diet is an important element of diabetes control. A diabetic diet on a budget focus on selecting healthy and cheap options.

When developing a low-cost diabetic diet, it is critical to consider both the cost of food and its nutritional content. This involves choosing whole meals that are low in added sugars, harmful fats, and salt. Fresh fruits and vegetables, lean proteins, whole grains, and low-fat dairy products should form the basis of a diabetic-friendly diet.

Meal planning is a vital tool for adhering to a diabetic diet that is cost-effective. Individuals can minimize impulsive purchases by preparing their meals ahead of time and ensuring they have the required components on hand. It also promotes better portion control and helps to maintain a balanced diet.

Portion management is essential for controlling blood sugar and keeping a healthy weight. It entails consuming the appropriate amount of food to ensure enough nutrients without overindulging. Measuring quantities with measuring cups, spoons, or a food scale can help people remain on track and avoid consuming extra calories.

Grocery shopping on a budget necessitates careful preparation and informed decisions. Individuals may maximize their restricted budget by looking for deals, discounts, and coupons. Buying in bulk and using store-brand items can also help you save money. Reading product labels and comparing costs is essential for making educated selections.

Following a low-cost diabetic diet has various advantages. First and foremost, it aids in the achievement and maintenance of better blood sugar management. People can avoid blood sugar rises by eating meals with a low glycemic index and regulating their portion sizes. This can help to lower the risk of diabetic complications.

Second, a diabetic diet that is reasonably priced can help with weight management. Individuals can reach and maintain a healthy weight by eating complete, nutrient-dense meals and controlling their portion sizes. This is significant since extra weight can exacerbate insulin resistance and raise the likelihood of problems.

Finally, choosing a low-cost diabetic diet supports general good health. Individuals who consume a range of healthy meals may guarantee that their bodies receive all of the vital vitamins, minerals, and antioxidants they require. This can strengthen the immune system, increase energy levels, and improve general health.

CHAPTER 2: UNDERSTANDING DIABETES

To begin, it is important to grasp the basic concept of diabetes. Diabetes is a chronic disease characterized by high levels of glucose (sugar) in the blood. This happens when the body doesn't create enough insulin, a hormone that regulates blood sugar, or when the cells don't respond correctly to insulin.

Understanding the various forms of diabetes is critical in controlling the disease. There are two forms of diabetes: type 1 and type 2. Type 1 diabetes is an autoimmune illness in which the body's immune system incorrectly assaults and destroys insulin-producing cells in the pancreas. Type 2 diabetes, on the other hand, is frequently linked to lifestyle factors including obesity, a poor diet, and a lack of exercise.

Diabetes is managed with a mix of lifestyle changes, medication, and regular blood sugar testing. Individuals with diabetes should eat a good diet, exercise regularly, and take their medicines as advised. Monitoring blood sugar levels helps people to keep track of their glucose levels and make changes to their treatment plan.

In addition to lifestyle changes, medication is essential in diabetes control. Depending on the type and severity of diabetes, people may need insulin injections or oral drugs to keep their blood sugar levels under control. It is critical to collaborate closely with a healthcare practitioner to identify the most appropriate pharmaceutical regimen.

Education and support are also important aspects of diabetes treatment. Understanding the effects of food, exercise, and medicine on blood sugar levels allows people to take control of their own health. Individuals with diabetes can benefit greatly from support groups and educational opportunities.

Types of Diabetes

Diabetes is a complex metabolic disorder that affects millions of people worldwide. This topic delves into the various types of diabetes, including Type 1, Type 2, and gestational diabetes. Each kind has its own unique traits that necessitate appropriate management tactics.

Type 1 diabetes, also known as insulin-dependent diabetes, is an autoimmune disease in which the immune system erroneously assaults and kills insulin-producing cells in the pancreas. This causes a shortage of insulin, a hormone required to regulate blood sugar levels. To maintain their blood sugar levels, people with Type 1 diabetes must get insulin injections on a regular basis or utilize an insulin pump. This kind of diabetes is usually diagnosed in childhood or early adulthood.

Type 2 diabetes, on the other hand, is a metabolic condition defined by insulin resistance and decreased insulin production. It is frequently connected with lifestyle variables such as poor nutrition, sedentary activity, and obesity. Unlike Type 1 diabetes, Type 2 diabetes may frequently be controlled via lifestyle changes such as a nutritious diet, regular exercise, and weight loss. In certain circumstances, oral medicines or insulin treatment may be necessary to regulate blood sugar levels.

Gestational diabetes develops during pregnancy and affects between 2 and 10% of pregnant women. It is caused by hormonal changes that interfere with the body's ability to adequately utilize insulin. Gestational diabetes often recovers after childbirth, but it raises the risk of acquiring Type 2 diabetes later in life. Managing gestational diabetes entails monitoring blood sugar levels, eating a healthy diet, and, in some situations, administering insulin.

It is crucial to highlight that, while the causes and management options for each type of diabetes differ, the ultimate aim is the same: to maintain healthy blood sugar levels. Regular blood sugar testing, adherence to medication or insulin regimens, and lifestyle changes are critical for successful diabetes control. Early diagnosis and intervention are crucial in preventing complications and improving long-term outcomes.

Blood Glucose Monitoring

Blood glucose monitoring plays a crucial role in the management of diabetes. It involves regularly checking blood glucose levels to ensure they are within the target range. This topic provides in-depth information on the significance of blood glucose monitoring and the available methods.

Monitoring blood glucose levels is necessary for a variety of reasons. For starters, it helps diabetics understand how their body reacts to certain diets, physical exercise, and medications. They can make more educated food, exercise, and medicine decisions if they check their glucose levels.

Regular blood glucose monitoring also aids in detecting patterns and trends in glucose levels. This information can be utilized to modify treatment strategies and make required lifestyle changes. For example, if a person routinely has high blood glucose levels after eating a certain type of food, they can avoid or limit their intake.

There are several ways for measuring blood glucose levels. The blood glucose meter is one of the most frequent methods. This mobile gadget detects glucose levels in a tiny blood sample collected by pricking the finger with a lancet. The blood sample is then placed on a test strip, which is introduced into the meter for examination. Blood glucose meters deliver rapid readings and are portable, making them ideal for everyday monitoring.

Another option is a continuous glucose monitoring (CGM) device. A tiny sensor implanted beneath the skin measures glucose levels in the interstitial fluid. The sensor automatically sends glucose measurements to a receiver or smartphone app. CGM devices deliver real-time glucose readings, allowing users to see patterns and make prompt changes to their treatment regimen.

Flash glucose monitoring is another new approach. It entails wearing a tiny sensor on the back of the upper arm that constantly monitors glucose levels in the interstitial fluid. Glucose measurements are collected by scanning the sensor with a reader or smartphone. Flash glucose monitoring gives retroactive glucose data, allowing users to analyze their glucose levels over a defined time period.

The frequency of blood glucose monitoring is determined by several factors, including the type of diabetes and the individual's treatment plan. People with type 1 diabetes often need to check their blood glucose levels many times each day, particularly before meals, after meals, and before bedtime. Type 2 diabetics may need less frequent testing, depending on their medication regimen and overall glucose control.

Target blood glucose levels vary according to the individual and their circumstances. Healthcare practitioners frequently specify goal ranges, which may differ for fasting glucose, pre-meal glucose, and post-meal glucose. These goal ranges assist people maintain optimum glucose management and lower their risk of problems.

Understanding the numerical numbers and their consequences is essential when interpreting blood glucose levels. High blood glucose levels, commonly known as hyperglycemia, might suggest insufficient insulin or prescription dose, excessive carbohydrate consumption, a lack of physical exercise, or disease. Hypoglycemia, or low blood glucose levels, can be caused by taking too much insulin or medicine, skipping or delaying meals, increasing physical activity, or consuming alcohol. Understanding these patterns helps individuals make informed decisions to manage their diabetes effectively.

Meal Timing and Diabetes

Meal timing plays a crucial role in managing blood sugar levels for individuals with diabetes. Understanding the relevance of meal timing is essential for effective diabetes management.

The time of meals can affect blood sugar levels because carbohydrates in food are broken down into glucose, which is subsequently absorbed into the circulation. This causes a rise in blood glucose levels. Individuals with diabetes can maintain their blood sugar levels and avoid issues by scheduling meals correctly.

Consistency is a key part of meal scheduling. It is advisable to eat at regular intervals and space them out equally throughout the day. This contributes to steady blood sugar levels and minimizes rapid changes. Irregular meal timings can cause unpredictable blood sugar fluctuations, making it difficult to successfully control diabetes.

Another aspect is the timing of carbohydrate consumption. Carbohydrates are important for energy, but the kind and amount ingested might have an impact on blood sugar levels. It is preferable to distribute carbohydrate consumption evenly throughout the day rather than eating a significant quantity in one session. This strategy helps to avoid rapid rises in blood sugar levels and allows for improved blood sugar management.

Additionally, the timing of meals in relation to medicine is critical. Some diabetic treatments, such as insulin, perform best when taken with or right before a meal. This helps to time the medication's maximal action with the rise in blood sugar levels after eating. To ensure best blood sugar management, follow your healthcare provider's advice for medication and meal time.

By incorporating these strategies into their daily routine, individuals with diabetes can effectively manage their blood sugar levels and reduce the risk of complications.

Exercise and Diabetes

Exercise plays a crucial role in managing diabetes and controlling blood sugar levels. Regular physical activity has numerous positive effects on individuals with diabetes, including improved insulin sensitivity, reduced risk of complications, and overall better health and well-being.

One of the primary advantages of exercise for people with diabetes is its potential to help manage blood sugar levels. During physical exercise, the body's muscles burn glucose for energy, which helps to reduce blood sugar levels. Regular exercise can help improve insulin sensitivity, allowing the body to use insulin more efficiently and keep blood sugar levels steady.

In addition to improving blood sugar management, exercise can lower the risk of diabetic complications. Regular physical exercise can enhance cardiovascular health, lower blood pressure, and minimize the risk of heart disease, which is a significant side effect of diabetes. Exercise can also help with weight management since it burns calories and increases lean muscle mass. Individuals with diabetes should maintain a healthy weight since excess weight might make blood sugar levels more difficult to regulate.

Furthermore, research has demonstrated that exercise improves mental health and general well-being. Physical exercise produces endorphins, or "feel-good" chemicals that can help relieve stress, anxiety, and sadness. Regular exercise can also help with sleep quality, energy levels, mood, and cognitive function.

When adding exercise into a diabetes care strategy, several aspects must be considered. Individuals with diabetes should check with their healthcare provider before beginning any new fitness routine to verify that it is safe and appropriate for their unique requirements. It is also critical to check blood sugar levels prior to, during, and after exercise to avoid hypoglycemia or hyperglycemia. Adjustments to medication or carbohydrate consumption may be required to keep blood sugar constant during physical exercise.

By incorporating regular physical activity into their lifestyle, individuals with diabetes can effectively manage their condition and lead a healthier, more active life.

Stress Management

Stress management plays a crucial role in effectively managing diabetes and maintaining stable blood sugar levels. High levels of stress can have a negative impact on blood sugar control and overall health. Therefore, it is important for individuals with diabetes to incorporate stress management techniques into their daily routine.

One of the most effective stress management techniques is exercise. Regular physical activity not only helps regulate blood sugar levels, as previously mentioned, but also releases endorphins, which are natural mood boosters. Exercise can help reduce stress, anxiety, and depression, improving overall mental well-being.

In addition to exercise, relaxation techniques such as deep breathing exercises, meditation, and yoga can also be beneficial in managing stress. These techniques help activate the body's relaxation response, reducing stress hormones and promoting a sense of calmness.

Another important aspect of stress management is maintaining a healthy lifestyle. This includes getting enough sleep, eating a balanced diet, and avoiding unhealthy habits such as smoking and excessive alcohol consumption. Adequate sleep is essential for managing stress and maintaining overall health.

Engaging in hobbies and activities that bring joy and relaxation can also help in managing stress. This could include activities such as painting, gardening, listening to music, or spending time with loved ones. Finding time for oneself and engaging in activities that promote relaxation and happiness can significantly reduce stress levels.

It is important to remember that stress management is not a one-size-fits-all approach. What works for one person may not work for another. It is essential to explore different stress management techniques and find what works best for each individual.

Support and Resources

This topic focuses on the support and resources available for individuals managing diabetes. It emphasizes the importance of accessing these resources to enhance diabetes management and improve overall well-being.

One important part of assistance and resources is the availability of instructional materials. These materials give useful information on diabetes, its treatment, and lifestyle adjustments that can help. They discuss healthy nutrition, exercise, blood sugar monitoring, and medication management. Educational materials might take the shape of brochures, pamphlets, books, or internet tools. They are intended to provide individuals with knowledge and the skills they need to effectively manage their diabetes.

In addition to instructional resources, there are several internet tools and apps that may help people monitor and manage their diabetes. These apps frequently incorporate features like blood sugar monitoring, meal planning, medication reminders, and tailored health advice. They offer an easy and accessible tool to keep track of diabetes management responsibilities and make educated lifestyle decisions. Online tools and applications may be accessed via smartphones, tablets, or laptops, making them convenient for those on the go.

Individuals living with diabetes benefit greatly from support groups, which offer emotional support and direction. These communities bring together people who have had similar experiences and struggles with diabetes. They create a secure and sympathetic atmosphere in which people may express their worries, seek assistance, and learn from one another. Support groups may be either in-person or virtual, allowing people to connect with others no matter where they are. They frequently have monthly meetings, educational programs, and social gatherings to build a sense of community and continuing support.

There are also various groups dedicated to helping people with diabetes. These groups provide a variety of services, including advocacy, education, and financial help. They seek to raise diabetes awareness, promote research into improved treatment choices, and advocate for diabetic-friendly policy. These organizations frequently provide helplines and websites where people may get information, seek support, and connect with professionals in their fields.

Individuals must actively seek out and interact with these assistance and services in order to fully benefit from them. This can be accomplished by contacting healthcare providers for advice, performing online research, or seeking references from other diabetics. It is also crucial to monitor for updates and new materials as they become available. By utilizing these support and resources, individuals can enhance their diabetes management, stay motivated, and improve their overall quality of life.

CHAPTER 3: MEDICATIONS AND INSULIN

This chapter explores the crucial role that medications and insulin play in the effective management of diabetes. Individuals with varying levels of knowledge and understanding will find valuable information in this section.

Medications are a crucial part of diabetes management, particularly for those with type 2 diabetes. They function by regulating blood sugar levels and increasing insulin sensitivity. There are several kinds of drugs available, each with its unique mechanism of action and advantages. These include oral treatments like metformin, sulfonylureas, and DPP-4 inhibitors, as well as injectables such GLP-1 receptor agonists and SGLT2 inhibitors.

Insulin, on the other hand, is a hormone that controls blood sugar levels. It is generally used to treat type 1 diabetes, but it may also be administered to people with type 2 diabetes who need additional help maintaining their blood sugar levels. Insulin treatment is the process of administering insulin via injections or insulin pumps. Individual needs can be met with a variety of insulin types, including rapid-acting, short-acting, intermediate-acting, and long-acting.

Understanding the numerous drugs and insulin alternatives is critical for diabetics to successfully manage their disease. It is critical to collaborate closely with healthcare providers to select the best drugs and insulin regimen depending on individual needs, lifestyle, and general health.

In this chapter, we'll look at the mechanisms of action, advantages, and potential adverse effects of several diabetic medicines including insulin. We will also examine crucial factors for medication adherence, dose modifications, and potential drug interactions.. Additionally, we will explore the latest advancements in medication and insulin therapies, including emerging treatments and technologies that aim to enhance diabetes management.

Medications for Diabetes

Medications play a crucial role in the management of diabetes. They are used to help regulate blood sugar levels and prevent complications associated with the disease. This topic provides a comprehensive understanding of medications used in diabetes treatment and their mechanisms.

There are various types of medications available. One common type is oral medications, which are taken by mouth. These medications work by stimulating the pancreas to produce more insulin, increasing insulin sensitivity, or reducing the amount of glucose produced by the liver. Some examples of oral medications include metformin, sulfonylureas, and thiazolidinediones.

Insulin is another key type of drug used to treat diabetes. Insulin is a hormone that regulates blood sugar levels by enabling glucose into cells for energy. Individuals with diabetes have either insufficient insulin production or inefficient insulin usage. Insulin treatment entails injecting insulin into the body to replace or boost the body's own insulin production. As previously stated, insulin is classified into four types: rapid-acting, short-acting, intermediate-acting, and long-acting insulin. Each kind has a distinct start and duration of action, allowing for tailored insulin regimens depending on individual requirements.

In addition to oral medicines and insulin, injectable drugs are used to treat diabetes. These drugs are usually used in combination with other medications, such as insulin, to help regulate blood sugar levels. Injectable treatments include GLP-1 receptor agonists, which increase insulin production while decreasing glucagon secretion, and SGLT2 inhibitors, which lower blood sugar levels by increasing glucose excretion in the urine.

Each medicine used in diabetes therapy has a distinct mechanism of action. Metformin, for example, works by lowering the amount of glucose generated by the liver while also boosting insulin sensitivity. Sulfonylureas cause the pancreas to secrete more insulin. Thiazolidinediones promote insulin sensitivity in muscle and fat cells. Insulin transports glucose into cells for energy.

Individuals with diabetes should consult with healthcare specialists to establish the best appropriate medicines and insulin regimen for their personal requirements. When selecting the appropriate drugs, consider age, general health, and lifestyle factors. Adherence to drug regimens is also essential for successful diabetes treatment.

When using diabetic medicines, it is critical to closely follow the dose directions. Medication doses may need to be modified in response to blood sugar levels and other variables. It is also crucial to be informed of any potential negative effects of these drugs. Common adverse effects include gastrointestinal problems, weight gain, and low blood sugar levels. Any side effects should be reported to healthcare specialists so that they can be properly managed.

New diabetic therapies and technology are constantly being developed. These might include new drugs with enhanced mechanisms of action or novel insulin delivery technologies like insulin pumps or continuous glucose monitoring devices. Staying up to date on these breakthroughs might help diabetics make more educated treatment decisions.

By adhering to medication regimens and staying informed about emerging treatments and technologies, individuals with diabetes can effectively manage their condition and improve their overall health.

Insulin Therapy

Insulin therapy plays a crucial role in the management of diabetes. It involves the use of insulin, a hormone that helps regulate blood sugar levels. This topic will provide readers with a comprehensive understanding of insulin therapy options, including different types of insulin and various administration methods.

There are several types of insulin available, which have been briefly touched upon. Each has its own onset, peak, and duration of action. Rapid-acting insulin, such as insulin lispro, acts quickly to lower blood sugar levels after a meal. Short-acting insulin, like regular insulin, takes effect within 30 minutes and lasts for a few hours. Intermediate-acting insulin, such as NPH insulin, has a longer duration of action, typically lasting up to 12 hours. Lastly, long-acting insulin, like insulin glargine, provides a steady release of insulin over a prolonged period, often lasting up to 24 hours.

In terms of administration methods, insulin can be delivered through insulin injections, insulin pens, or insulin pumps. Insulin injections involve using a syringe to inject insulin into the fatty tissue just beneath the skin. Insulin pens are pre-filled devices that allow for easy and convenient insulin administration. They are particularly useful for individuals who require multiple daily injections. Insulin pumps, on the other hand, are small devices that deliver a continuous supply of insulin through a catheter placed under the skin. They offer precise insulin dosing and can be programmed to deliver bolus doses of insulin before meals.

Insulin therapy is essential for individuals with type 1 diabetes, as their bodies do not produce insulin. It is also commonly used in individuals with type 2 diabetes who have difficulty managing their blood sugar levels through lifestyle modifications and oral medications alone. Insulin therapy helps regulate blood sugar levels, prevent complications, and improve overall glycemic control.

Choosing the most suitable insulin therapy option depends on individual needs and preferences. Factors to consider include lifestyle, blood sugar control goals, injection comfort, and individual schedule. It is important to work closely with healthcare professionals, such as endocrinologists or diabetes educators, to determine the most appropriate insulin therapy regimen.

Adherence to insulin therapy is crucial for successful diabetes management. It is important to follow the prescribed insulin regimen, including the correct dosage and timing of insulin administration. Regular monitoring of blood sugar levels is also necessary to ensure optimal glycemic control.

Staying informed about emerging treatments and technologies in diabetes management is essential. Continuous advancements in insulin therapy have led to the development of new insulin analogs and delivery devices, providing individuals with more options to customize their treatment plans.

Adherence to the prescribed insulin regimen and staying informed about advancements in diabetes management are essential for optimal glycemic control and overall well-being.

Medication Management

Managing diabetes medications is an essential aspect of effectively controlling this chronic condition. Proper medication management plays a crucial role in maintaining blood sugar levels within the target range and preventing complications associated with diabetes. This comprehensive guide provides practical tips and strategies for managing diabetes medications, ensuring that individuals with diabetes can optimize their treatment plan and lead a healthy life.

1. Understand Your Medications:
To effectively manage diabetes medications, it is crucial to have a comprehensive understanding of the medications prescribed by your healthcare provider. Familiarize yourself with the names, dosages, and potential side effects of each medication. This knowledge will empower you to take an active role in your treatment and make informed decisions.

2. Follow Medication Instructions:
Adhering to the prescribed medication regimen is vital for successful diabetes management. Take your medications at the recommended times and in the correct dosages. If you have any doubts or concerns about your medications, consult your healthcare provider for clarification.

3. Create a Medication Schedule:
To avoid missing doses or taking incorrect amounts of medication, create a medication schedule that fits your daily routine. Use reminders, such as alarms or smartphone apps, to help you stay on track. Consider organizing your medications in a pillbox labeled with the days of the week to ensure accuracy and consistency.

4. Store Medications Properly:
Proper storage of diabetes medications is essential to maintain their effectiveness. Follow the instructions provided by your pharmacist or healthcare provider regarding storage temperature and conditions. Keep medications away from direct sunlight and moisture, and ensure they are out of reach of children and pets.

5. Communicate with Your Healthcare Provider:
Regular communication with your healthcare provider is crucial for effective medication management. Keep them informed about any changes in your health, medication side effects, or difficulties in adhering to the prescribed regimen. Your healthcare provider can make adjustments to your treatment plan as needed.

6. Monitor Blood Sugar Levels:

Regularly monitoring your blood sugar levels helps you assess the effectiveness of your medication regimen. Keep a record of your readings and share them with your healthcare provider during check-ups. This information will assist in determining if any adjustments are necessary to achieve optimal blood sugar control.

7. Be Aware of Medication Interactions:
Some medications, including over-the-counter drugs and supplements, can interact with diabetes medications and affect their efficacy. Inform your healthcare provider about all the medications you are taking, including herbal remedies and supplements, to avoid potential interactions.

8. Educate Yourself on Insulin Therapy:
In addition to oral medications, insulin therapy is a common treatment for diabetes. Understanding the different types of insulin, their onset and duration of action, and the methods of administration is essential. Work closely with your healthcare provider to determine the appropriate insulin regimen for your specific needs.

By implementing these practical tips and strategies, individuals with diabetes can take control of their health and lead fulfilling lives.

CHAPTER 4: LIFESTYLE AND DIABETES

Diet plays a vital role in managing diabetes. The chapter examines the importance of a balanced and nutritious diet that includes the right proportion of carbohydrates, proteins, and fats. It also explores the impact of different types of carbohydrates on blood sugar levels, emphasizing the significance of portion control and mindful eating. The chapter further discusses the benefits of incorporating high-fiber foods, lean proteins, and healthy fats into one's diet to promote stable blood sugar levels.

Regular physical activity is another crucial aspect of diabetes management. The chapter highlights the positive effects of exercise on insulin sensitivity and blood sugar control. It provides insights into different types of exercises, including aerobic activities, strength training, and flexibility exercises, and their respective benefits for individuals with diabetes. Additionally, the chapter emphasizes the importance of incorporating physical activity into daily routines and offers practical tips for staying active.

Stress management is an often overlooked but essential component of diabetes management. The chapter explores the connection between stress and blood sugar levels, highlighting the impact of stress hormones on insulin resistance. It provides strategies for stress reduction, such as relaxation techniques, mindfulness practices, and engaging in hobbies or activities that promote emotional well-being.

The chapter also addresses the significance of sleep patterns in diabetes management. It discusses the relationship between sleep deprivation, insulin resistance, and glucose metabolism. The importance of establishing a consistent sleep routine and adopting healthy sleep habits is emphasized, along with tips for improving sleep quality.

Furthermore, this chapter offers practical recommendations for adopting a healthy lifestyle to prevent and manage diabetes. It provides guidance on setting realistic goals, creating action plans, and seeking support from healthcare professionals and support groups. The chapter also highlights the importance of regular monitoring of blood sugar levels and medication adherence.

Diet and Nutrition

Diet and nutrition play a crucial role in managing diabetes effectively. The food we consume directly impacts our blood sugar levels, insulin sensitivity, and overall well-being. This sub-topic will conduct an in-depth exploration of the influence of diet and nutrition on diabetes management.

A healthy diet for individuals with diabetes focuses on balancing the intake of carbohydrates, proteins, and fats. Carbohydrates have the most significant impact on blood sugar levels, so it is essential to choose the right types and monitor portion sizes. Complex carbohydrates, such as whole grains, legumes, and vegetables, are preferred over simple carbohydrates like refined sugars and white flour products. These complex carbohydrates are digested more slowly, resulting in a gradual rise in blood sugar levels.

In addition to carbohydrates, proteins and fats also play a role in managing blood sugar levels. Proteins help in stabilizing blood sugar levels and provide a feeling of fullness. Good sources of protein include lean meats, poultry, fish, eggs, tofu, and legumes. Healthy fats, such as those found in avocados, nuts, seeds, and olive oil, are beneficial for heart health and should be consumed in moderation.

Fiber is another essential component of a diabetes-friendly diet. It helps in controlling blood sugar levels, promoting satiety, and maintaining a healthy digestive system. Foods rich in fiber include whole grains, fruits, vegetables, and legumes.

In terms of meal planning, individuals with diabetes can benefit from portion control and regular meal timings. Eating smaller, balanced meals throughout the day can help in preventing spikes in blood sugar levels. It is also important to avoid skipping meals, as this can lead to unstable blood sugar levels.

Apart from meal planning, it is crucial to pay attention to the glycemic index (GI) of foods. The GI measures how quickly a food raises blood sugar levels. Foods with a low GI are digested more slowly, resulting in a gradual increase in blood sugar levels. Examples of low GI foods include whole grains, non-starchy vegetables, and most fruits.

In addition to diet, proper hydration is essential for individuals with diabetes. Drinking an adequate amount of water helps in maintaining overall health and supports proper kidney function.

It is important to note that dietary needs may vary depending on individual factors, such as age, weight, activity level, and specific diabetes management goals. Consulting with a registered dietitian or healthcare provider can provide personalized guidance and recommendations.

Proper hydration and personalized guidance from healthcare professionals are also crucial in achieving optimal diabetes management through diet and nutrition.

Physical Activity

Regular physical activity plays a crucial role in managing blood sugar levels for individuals with diabetes. Engaging in regular exercise helps to improve insulin sensitivity, allowing the body to use insulin more effectively. This, in turn, helps to regulate blood sugar levels and reduce the risk of complications associated with diabetes.

When it comes to physical activity, there are various options to choose from. Aerobic exercises such as brisk walking, jogging, swimming, and cycling are highly beneficial for individuals with diabetes. These exercises increase heart rate and breathing, helping to burn calories and improve cardiovascular health.

Strength training exercises are also important for individuals with diabetes. These exercises involve working against resistance, such as lifting weights or using resistance bands. Strength training helps to build muscle mass, which can improve insulin sensitivity and promote better blood sugar control.

In addition to aerobic and strength training exercises, flexibility exercises are also recommended. These exercises include stretching and yoga, which help to improve flexibility, balance, and overall mobility. Flexibility exercises can be particularly helpful for individuals with diabetes who may experience complications such as joint stiffness or neuropathy.

It is important to note that before starting any exercise program, individuals with diabetes should consult with their healthcare professional. They can provide personalized guidance on the type, duration, and intensity of exercise that is suitable for each individual's specific needs and health condition.

To maximize the benefits of physical activity, it is recommended to aim for at least 150 minutes of moderate-intensity aerobic activity per week, spread across several days. This can be achieved by engaging in activities such as brisk walking for 30 minutes, five days a week. Alternatively, individuals can opt for 75 minutes of vigorous-intensity aerobic activity per week, combined with strength training exercises at least two days a week.

It is important to monitor blood sugar levels before, during, and after exercise, especially for individuals taking insulin or certain diabetes medications. This helps to ensure that blood sugar levels remain within a safe range during physical activity. It may be necessary to adjust medication dosages or have a snack before exercising to prevent hypoglycemia.

Regular physical activity not only helps to control blood sugar levels but also offers numerous other health benefits. It can help to manage weight, reduce the risk of cardiovascular diseases, improve blood pressure and cholesterol levels, enhance mood, and boost overall well-being.

Sleep and Diabetes

Quality sleep plays a crucial role in effectively managing diabetes. The relationship between sleep and diabetes is significant, as adequate sleep has a direct impact on blood sugar levels and overall diabetes management. Understanding the importance of sleep and implementing strategies to improve sleep quality can greatly benefit individuals with diabetes.

Research has shown that insufficient sleep can lead to increased insulin resistance and higher blood sugar levels. Lack of sleep affects the body's ability to properly regulate glucose, resulting in elevated blood sugar levels. This can be particularly problematic for individuals with diabetes, as it can make blood sugar control more challenging.

To effectively manage diabetes, it is recommended that individuals aim for a consistent sleep duration of 7-9 hours per night. This optimal sleep duration helps regulate hormones involved in blood sugar control and promotes overall metabolic health. However, it is important to note that individual sleep needs may vary, and it is essential to find the right sleep duration that works best for each person.

Poor sleep quality can have detrimental effects on diabetes management. It can contribute to increased stress levels, impaired cognitive function, and decreased insulin sensitivity. Additionally, inadequate sleep can disrupt appetite-regulating hormones, leading to unhealthy food cravings and potential weight gain, which can further complicate diabetes management.

To improve sleep quality and better manage diabetes, several strategies can be implemented. Establishing a consistent sleep routine, including a regular bedtime and wake-up time, can help regulate the body's internal clock and promote better sleep. Creating a sleep-friendly environment, such as keeping the bedroom cool, dark, and quiet, can also contribute to better sleep quality.

Engaging in relaxation techniques before bedtime, such as deep breathing exercises or meditation, can help calm the mind and promote relaxation. It is also important to avoid stimulating activities, such as intense exercise or consuming caffeine, close to bedtime, as they can interfere with sleep.

Incorporating regular physical activity into daily routines can also positively impact sleep quality. Exercise promotes better sleep by reducing stress levels, improving mood, and increasing overall physical tiredness.

By prioritizing and implementing strategies to improve sleep quality, individuals with diabetes can better manage their condition and improve their overall well-being.

Emotional Well-Being

Diabetes not only affects the physical health of individuals, but it also has a significant impact on their emotional well-being. Managing a chronic condition like diabetes can be challenging and can lead to various emotional challenges. This subtopic delves into the emotional elements of diabetes and offers solutions for dealing with the disease's psychological effects.

Diabetes may be stressful since it demands frequent blood sugar testing, adherence to medication and treatment programs, and lifestyle changes. The burden of controlling diabetes can cause anxiety and even depression in some people. It is critical to recognize and manage these emotional difficulties in order to sustain overall well-being.

Developing good stress-coping methods is an important element of maintaining emotional well-being. Diabetes-related stress can be caused by concerns about blood sugar control, the risk of complications, or the difficulty of self-management. Learning stress management strategies such as deep breathing exercises, meditation, or indulging in hobbies can help people cope with the problems of diabetes.

Additionally, a robust support system is required. Connecting with other diabetics can bring a sense of belonging and understanding. Support groups or online communities can provide a forum for sharing experiences, seeking guidance, and receiving emotional support. Family and friends can also provide valuable support and understanding.

Another crucial part of emotional well-being is dealing with anxiety or sadness that may occur as a result of living with diabetes. It is critical to recognize the symptoms of these illnesses and get expert assistance if necessary. Mental health specialists can help you manage diabetes-related anxiety and despair.

Regular physical activity can also improve your mental well-being. As previously stated, exercise produces endorphins, sometimes known as "feel-good" chemicals. These endorphins can boost mood and lessen stress. Finding a fun physical activity and putting it into your daily routine may have a big influence on your mental health.

To summarize, treating the emotional elements of diabetes is critical for overall well-being.. By developing effective coping strategies for stress, seeking support from others, addressing anxiety or depression, and engaging in regular physical activity, individuals with diabetes can better manage the emotional challenges associated with the disease. Prioritizing emotional well-being alongside physical health is essential for a balanced and fulfilling life with diabetes.

Social Support

Social support, which has been briefly touched upon in the previous section, plays a crucial role in the management of diabetes. Having a robust support system can greatly impact the overall well-being and outcomes of individuals living with diabetes. This topic emphasizes the importance of seeking and maintaining social support in diabetes management.

One of the key benefits of social support is its positive impact on emotional well-being. Living with diabetes can be emotionally challenging, and having a strong network of family, friends, and healthcare professionals can provide individuals with the emotional support they need. This support can help individuals cope with the stress and anxiety that often accompany diabetes, leading to improved mental health.

In addition to emotional support, social support also plays a vital role in motivating individuals to adhere to their treatment plans. When individuals have people around them who understand and support their diabetes management efforts, they are more likely to stay motivated and committed to their treatment regimen. This can lead to better blood sugar control and overall improvement in diabetes outcomes.

Seeking social support can be done in various ways. Online communities and forums provide a platform for individuals to connect with others who are going through similar experiences. These communities offer a space for sharing knowledge, exchanging tips, and providing emotional support. Local support groups also offer an opportunity for individuals to meet face-to-face with others who understand the challenges of living with diabetes. These groups often organize educational sessions, guest speakers, and social events to foster a sense of community and support.

Counseling services can also be beneficial for individuals who need professional support in managing the emotional aspects of diabetes. Diabetes educators and counselors can provide guidance on coping strategies, stress management techniques, and dealing with anxiety or depression. These services can help individuals develop effective strategies to navigate the emotional challenges that come with diabetes.

Educational programs are another avenue for seeking social support. These programs provide individuals with the opportunity to learn more about diabetes management, connect with healthcare professionals, and meet others who share similar experiences. Educational programs often cover topics such as healthy eating, physical activity, medication management, and blood sugar monitoring. By participating in these programs, individuals can gain knowledge, build relationships, and find support in their diabetes journey.

By building a strong support system, individuals can enhance their ability to cope with the challenges of living with diabetes and lead a balanced and fulfilling life.

Travel and Diabetes

Traveling can be an exciting and fulfilling experience, but for individuals with diabetes, it requires careful planning and preparation to ensure their health is maintained throughout the trip. This topic provides valuable tips and information for individuals traveling with diabetes to help them manage their condition effectively while on the go.

One of the key aspects of traveling with diabetes is managing blood sugar levels. It is important to monitor blood sugar levels regularly, especially during travel, as changes in routine, activity levels, and meal times can affect blood sugar levels. Individuals should work closely with their healthcare team to establish target blood sugar ranges and adjust medication dosages accordingly.

When traveling, it is essential to pack all necessary medications and supplies. This includes carrying extra insulin, syringes or insulin pens, blood glucose monitoring devices, test strips, and any other medications prescribed by the healthcare provider. It is advisable to carry these supplies in a carry-on bag to ensure they are easily accessible and not affected by extreme temperatures in the cargo hold.

Planning meals and snacks is another crucial aspect of managing diabetes while traveling. Individuals should research and familiarize themselves with the food options available at their travel destination. It is recommended to pack healthy snacks such as nuts, fruits, and granola bars to have on hand in case of limited food choices or delays in meals. It is also important to stay hydrated by drinking plenty of water and avoiding sugary beverages.

Dealing with time zone changes can pose a challenge for individuals with diabetes. It is recommended to consult with a healthcare provider to determine the appropriate adjustments in medication dosages and meal timings to account for the time zone changes. Adhering to the new schedule as closely as possible can help in maintaining stable blood sugar levels.

Carrying identification and medical information is crucial for individuals with diabetes, especially when traveling. It is recommended to wear a medical alert bracelet or necklace that indicates the individual's condition and provides emergency contact information. Additionally, carrying a written list of medications, emergency contact numbers, and healthcare provider information can be helpful in case of any medical emergencies.

Managing stress and staying active during travel is also important for individuals with diabetes. Engaging in stress-relieving activities such as deep breathing exercises, meditation, or yoga can help in managing stress levels. It is also advisable to incorporate physical activity into the travel itinerary, such as walking tours, swimming, or hiking, to stay active and maintain blood sugar control.

CHAPTER 5: BUDGET-FRIENDLY DIABETIC DIET BASICS

When it comes to managing diabetes on a budget, making smart food choices is essential. This chapter provides valuable information on affordable food options that are suitable for individuals with diabetes. It emphasizes the importance of incorporating fresh fruits and vegetables, lean proteins, whole grains, and low-fat dairy products into the diet. These food choices not only provide essential nutrients but also help in managing blood sugar levels effectively.

Meal planning plays a crucial role in maintaining a budget-friendly diabetic diet. This chapter offers practical tips and strategies for planning meals that are both healthy and cost-effective. It encourages individuals to create a weekly meal plan, make a shopping list, and stick to it while grocery shopping. By planning meals in advance, individuals can avoid impulsive purchases and ensure that they have all the necessary ingredients for their diabetic-friendly meals.

Portion control is another key aspect of a budget-friendly diabetic diet. This chapter provides guidance on how to control portion sizes without compromising on nutrition. It emphasizes the importance of measuring food portions and being mindful of serving sizes. By practicing portion control, individuals can manage their calorie intake and maintain a healthy weight, which is crucial for diabetes management.

In addition to food choices and portion control, this chapter also focuses on cost-effective cooking methods. It provides tips on cooking techniques that require minimal oil and use affordable ingredients. By opting for methods such as baking, grilling, or steaming, individuals can reduce the use of unhealthy fats and save money on cooking oils.

Lastly, this chapter highlights the significance of monitoring blood sugar levels regularly. It emphasizes the need for individuals with diabetes to track their blood sugar levels to ensure that they are within the target range. By regularly monitoring blood sugar levels, individuals can make necessary adjustments to their diet and medication if needed, thereby maintaining optimal diabetes management.

Meal Planning on a Budget

Meal planning is an essential aspect of managing diabetes, especially when dealing with budget constraints. Planning meals in advance not only helps individuals save money but also ensures that they make the most out of their limited resources. This topic will provide valuable insights and tips on how to create budget-friendly meal plans, strategies for shopping on a budget, and the benefits of meal planning in terms of saving money and reducing food waste.

Creating a budget-friendly meal plan starts with making smart food choices. Opting for affordable yet nutritious foods is key. Staples such as whole grains, legumes, and seasonal fruits and vegetables are not only cost-effective but also provide essential nutrients. Including lean proteins like chicken, fish, and tofu can also be a budget-friendly option.

When planning meals on a budget, portion control plays a crucial role. It helps individuals manage their food intake while ensuring that they get the necessary nutrients. By controlling portion sizes, individuals can reduce food waste and stretch their budget further.

Another strategy for meal planning on a budget is to utilize cost-effective cooking methods. Slow cooking, batch cooking, and using leftovers creatively can help individuals save both time and money. These methods allow for the preparation of larger quantities of food, which can be divided into portions and enjoyed throughout the week.

Shopping wisely is essential when trying to stick to a budget. Prioritizing essential items and comparing prices can help individuals make informed decisions. Buying in bulk, especially for non-perishable items, can also lead to significant savings. Additionally, taking advantage of sales, discounts, and coupons can further reduce expenses.

Meal planning on a budget not only helps individuals save money but also reduces food waste. By planning meals in advance, individuals can utilize ingredients efficiently, ensuring that nothing goes to waste. Leftovers may be recycled into new dishes or frozen for later use, minimizing the need to buy more ingredients.

As has been made clear, regularly monitoring blood sugar levels is crucial for individuals with diabetes. Meal planning allows for better control and understanding of how different foods affect blood sugar levels. By following a well-balanced meal plan, individuals can maintain stable blood sugar levels and reduce the risk of complications.

Smart Grocery Shopping

This topic focuses on smart grocery shopping techniques that can help individuals manage their diabetes on a budget. It provides strategies and tips for budget-conscious grocery shopping, ensuring that individuals can make cost-effective choices while still maintaining a nutritious diet. By following these techniques, individuals can save money and reduce food waste.

One important aspect of smart grocery shopping is meal planning. Planning meals ahead of time allows people to make more educated food choices and prevent impulse purchases. Meal planning involves creating a weekly or monthly menu and identifying the necessary ingredients. This helps individuals to buy only what they need and avoid excess spending.

Creating a shopping list is another crucial step in smart grocery shopping. A well-prepared shopping list ensures that individuals purchase all the necessary items and avoid buying unnecessary or unhealthy foods. The list should include items for planned meals, as well as essential pantry staples.

Comparing prices is an effective way to save money while grocery shopping. Individuals should take the time to evaluate pricing from different brands and retailers. This allows them to identify the most affordable options without compromising on quality. It is also important to consider unit prices, as sometimes buying in larger quantities can be more cost-effective.

Using coupons and taking advantage of discounts can significantly reduce grocery expenses. Individuals should look for coupons in newspapers, magazines, or online platforms. They can also sign up for loyalty programs or newsletters offered by grocery stores to receive special discounts and promotions. Utilizing these opportunities can lead to substantial savings.

Buying in bulk is another strategy for saving money on groceries. Purchasing non-perishable items, such as grains, legumes, and canned goods, in bulk can be more economical in the long run. However, it is important to consider storage space and consumption rates to avoid wastage.

Smart grocery shopping also involves being mindful of sales and seasonal produce. Keeping an eye out for sales and discounts allows individuals to stock up on essentials when prices are lower. Additionally, buying seasonal fruits and vegetables not only ensures freshness and flavor but also helps to reduce costs.

Lastly, individuals can explore cost-saving strategies such as purchasing store brands or generic products. These alternatives are often more affordable than name brands but can still provide the same nutritional value. It is important to read labels and compare the ingredients to ensure the quality of the product.

By implementing these smart grocery shopping techniques, individuals can effectively manage their diabetes on a budget. Planning meals, creating shopping lists, comparing prices, using coupons and discounts, buying in bulk, and considering store brands are all strategies that can help individuals save money while still maintaining a nutritious and balanced diet.

CHAPTER 6: COOKING ON A BUDGET

Meal planning is a crucial step in cooking on a budget. By planning your weekly meals ahead of time, you may minimize impulse purchases and reduce food waste. Start by assessing what you already have in your pantry and fridge, and then create a shopping list based on the ingredients you need. This way, you can make the most of sales and discounts, and avoid buying unnecessary items.

Using leftovers in inventive ways is an excellent strategy to extend your budget. Rather of wasting them, repurpose them into new meals. For example, leftover roasted chicken may be made into a tasty chicken salad or mixed into a stir-fry. Get creative and experiment with different flavor combinations to keep your meals exciting and varied.

Cooking in bulk and freezing meals is another strategy to save both time and money. Prepare larger batches of your favorite dishes and portion them into individual servings. These can be stored in the freezer for quick and convenient meals on busy days. Not only does this help you avoid expensive takeout, but it also ensures that you always have a homemade meal on hand.

Meal prepping is a game-changer for budget-friendly cooking. Set aside some time each week to prepare items beforehand. Chop vegetables, cook grains, and marinate proteins, so they are ready to use when you need them. This saves time during the week and reduces the temptation to order takeout or rely on convenience foods.

When it comes to ingredients, pantry staples and seasonal produce are your best friends. Pantry staples like beans, lentils, and canned tomatoes are affordable and versatile, making them perfect for budget-friendly cooking. Seasonal produce is not only fresher and more flavorful, but it is also less expensive. Incorporate seasonal fruits and veggies into your meals to increase variety while saving money.

Essential Kitchen Tools for Budget Cooking

To successfully cook on a budget, it is essential to have the right kitchen tools at your disposal. These tools not only make cooking easier and more efficient but also help you save money by enabling you to prepare meals from scratch. In this section, we will discuss the essential kitchen tools that are necessary for economical cooking.

1. Chef's Knife: A high-quality chef's knife is a must-have tool in any kitchen. It helps you to cut, slice, and dice items with accuracy, making meal preparation easier. Investing in a durable and sharp chef's knife will not only save you time but also ensure that you can easily handle a variety of ingredients.

2. Cutting Board: A sturdy cutting board is essential for safely and efficiently chopping ingredients. Opt for a cutting board made of wood or plastic, as they are durable and easy to clean. Having a separate cutting board for meat and vegetables is also recommended to prevent cross-contamination.

3. Mixing Bowls: A set of mixing bowls in different sizes is invaluable for a budget cook. These bowls can be used for mixing ingredients, marinating meat, or storing leftovers. Look for microwave and dishwasher-safe dishes for increased convenience. Measuring Cups and Spoons: Accurate measurements are crucial in cooking, especially when following recipes. Purchase a set of measuring cups and spoons to ensure that you add the appropriate amount of ingredients. This will help you avoid waste and achieve consistent results.

4. Non-Stick Cookware: Non-stick pans and pots are essential for cooking on a budget, as they require less oil or butter to prevent sticking. This not only reduces the amount of fat in your meals but also saves you money in the long run. Look for durable non-stick cookware that distributes heat evenly for optimal cooking results.

5. Oven Mitts: Protecting your hands from burns is essential when working with hot pots, pans, and baking dishes. Invest in a pair of heat-resistant oven mitts to ensure your safety in the kitchen. Look for mitts that provide a good grip and are comfortable to wear.

6. Baking Sheet: A baking sheet is a versatile tool that can be used for roasting vegetables, baking cookies, or reheating leftovers. Opt for a sturdy baking sheet that is easy to clean and has raised edges to prevent any spills or drips.

7. Blender or Food Processor: While not essential, a blender or food processor can be a valuable addition to your kitchen arsenal. It allows you to make homemade sauces, dips, and smoothies, saving you money on store-bought alternatives.

8. Can Opener: A reliable can opener is a must-have tool, especially if you frequently use canned ingredients such as beans, tomatoes, or tuna. Look for a can opener that is easy to use and durable.

9. Storage Containers: Having a collection of storage containers in various sizes is essential for storing leftovers and meal prepping. Opt for containers that are stackable, microwave-safe, and leak-proof to maximize their usefulness.

By equipping your kitchen with these essential tools, you will be well-prepared to cook delicious and budget-friendly meals. Remember to take care of your tools by cleaning them properly and storing them in a safe and organized manner. With the right kitchen tools, you can make the most of your ingredients and create satisfying meals without breaking the bank.

Batch Cooking and Freezing

Batch cooking and freezing are essential techniques for optimizing your budget and saving time in the kitchen. By preparing and storing meals in large quantities, you can ensure a constant supply of homemade meals while reducing food waste. This topic provides comprehensive instructions on batch cooking and freezing techniques, covering various steps and tips to help you efficiently prepare and store meals.

The first step in batch cooking is meal planning. Spend some time deciding the dishes you want to cook in quantity. Consider your family's favorite dishes, dietary restrictions, and the ingredients you have on hand. Make a list of the recipes you want to make and gather all the necessary ingredients.

Once you have your meal plan ready, it's time to start cooking. Begin by selecting a day or a few hours when you have ample time to dedicate to batch cooking. This will allow you to concentrate entirely on the subject at hand, with no interruptions. Gather all your essential kitchen tools, such as a chef's knife, cutting board, mixing bowls, measuring cups and spoons, non-stick cookware, oven mitts, and a baking sheet.

Follow your preferred recipes and create enormous quantities of food. Chop veggies, marinade meats, and prepare many recipes concurrently. This will save you time and energy in the long run. As you prepare each meal, divide it into individual portions using appropriate portioning tools, such as measuring cups or a kitchen scale. This ensures that each serving is uniform in size and easy to freeze.

After portioning, it's time to package and label your meals. Use high-quality freezer-safe and airtight storage containers. Divide the meals into individual containers, making sure to leave some headspace for expansion during freezing. Label each container with the dish's name and date of preparation. This will help you keep track of your inventory and ensure that you consume the meals before they expire.

Proper freezing methods are crucial to maintaining the quality and freshness of your meals. Allow the cooked meals to cool completely before placing them in the freezer. Place the containers in an ice bath or on a cooling rack to cool quickly. Once chilled, move the containers to the freezer and arrange them in an orderly manner to ensure appropriate air circulation. To ensure a stable freezing temperature, avoid overcrowding in the freezer. When it's time to enjoy your batch-cooked meals, simply thaw them in the refrigerator overnight or use the defrost setting on your microwave. Reheat the meals thoroughly before consuming, ensuring they reach a safe internal temperature.

Batch cooking and freezing offer numerous benefits, including saving time, reducing food waste, and providing a constant supply of homemade meals. By following these techniques and utilizing your essential kitchen tools, you can optimize your budget and make cooking a more efficient and enjoyable experience. Remember to clean your tools properly after each use and store them in an organized manner for easy access in future cooking endeavors.

Reducing Food Waste

Reducing food waste is a crucial aspect of sustainable living and responsible consumption. By employing efficient solutions, we may reduce food waste and optimize ingredient use. This not only helps to conserve resources but also saves money and reduces the environmental impact of food production.

Appropriate freezing methods play a crucial role in maximizing ingredient usage. Freezing food properly can help to preserve its quality and extend its shelf life. It is important to ensure that food is properly wrapped or stored in airtight containers to prevent freezer burn and maintain its taste and texture. By freezing ingredients such as fruits, vegetables, and meats, we can prolong their usability and reduce the likelihood of them going to waste.

Careful thawing and reheating are essential when using frozen ingredients. It is important to thaw food in the refrigerator or using the defrost function on the microwave to ensure even and safe thawing. Once thawed, food should be reheated thoroughly to eliminate any potential bacteria or pathogens. By following proper thawing and reheating techniques, we can safely utilize frozen ingredients and prevent any food waste that may occur due to improper handling.

Implementing these strategies not only reduces food waste but also brings several benefits. By minimizing waste, we can save money by utilizing the ingredients we have already purchased. Additionally, reducing food waste helps to conserve resources such as water, energy, and land that are used in food production. It also reduces the amount of waste that ends up in landfills, contributing to a cleaner and more sustainable environment.

While the above strategies provide a solid foundation for reducing food waste and maximizing ingredient usage, it is important to note that there are countless creative ways to implement these strategies in our daily lives. For example, using leftover vegetables to make a hearty soup or repurposing stale bread into delicious croutons. By being mindful of our food consumption and utilizing ingredients to their fullest potential, we can make a significant impact in reducing food waste and promoting a more sustainable future.

These strategies not only benefit our wallets but also contribute to a more sustainable and environmentally friendly way of living. Let's make a conscious effort to reduce food waste and make the most of the food we have.

CHAPTER 7: DIABETIC DIET BREAKFAST

Breakfast is often touted as the most important meal of the day, and this holds true for individuals with diabetes. It kickstarts the metabolism, regulates blood sugar levels, and provides the body with the necessary fuel to function optimally. By skipping breakfast, diabetics may experience blood sugar fluctuations, leading to increased hunger, overeating, and difficulty in managing diabetes effectively.

When it comes to a diabetic-friendly breakfast, the choice of ingredients is crucial. Opting for whole grains, such as oats, whole wheat bread, or quinoa, provides a slow release of carbohydrates, preventing rapid spikes in blood sugar levels. These complex carbs are also high in fiber, which improves digestion and regulates blood sugar levels.

Protein is another important part of a diabetic diet breakfast. Including sources like eggs, Greek yogurt, or cottage cheese can help stabilize blood sugar levels and provide a feeling of fullness. Protein also assists in building and repairing tissues, making it an essential part of a balanced meal.

In addition to whole grains and protein, healthy fats should be incorporated into the breakfast routine. Avocado, nuts, and seeds are excellent choices as they provide essential fatty acids and contribute to a feeling of satiety. These fats also help slow down the digestion of carbohydrates, preventing sudden spikes in blood sugar levels.

While selecting the right ingredients is important, portion control is equally vital. It is critical to find a balance and limit calorie consumption. Consulting a healthcare professional or a registered dietitian can help determine the appropriate portion sizes based on individual needs and goals.

Avoiding high-sugar options is crucial for individuals with diabetes. Sugary cereals, pastries, and sweetened beverages can cause a rapid increase in blood sugar levels. Instead, opt for natural sweeteners like stevia or incorporate fresh fruits to add a touch of sweetness to breakfast.

It is crucial to remember that each person's nutritional needs may differ. It is strongly advised to consult a healthcare expert or a certified dietitian before developing a tailored meal plan that takes into account unique needs, preferences, and overall health objectives. They can provide guidance on portion control, suggest suitable alternatives, and monitor progress over time.

CHAPTER 8: AFFORDABLE BREAKFAST RECIPES

---

1. Scrambled Eggs with Vegetables

Servings: 2
Preparation time: 5 minutes
Cooking time: 10 minutes
Ingredients:

- 4 large eggs
- 1/4 cup diced bell peppers (any color)
- 1/4 cup diced onions
- 1/4 cup diced tomatoes
- Salt and pepper to taste

Directions:

1. In a bowl, whisk the eggs until well beaten.

2. Heat a non-stick skillet over medium heat and spray with cooking spray.

3. Add the diced bell peppers, onions, and tomatoes to the skillet and sauté for 2-3 minutes until softened.

4. Pour the beaten eggs into the skillet and cook, stirring occasionally, until the eggs are cooked through.

5. Season with salt and pepper to taste.

Nutritional Values per Serving: Calories: 354 kcal; Protein: 25.8 g; Carbohydrates: 5g; Dietary Fiber: 1g; Total Fat: 10g; Saturated Fat: 3g; Cholesterol: 372mg; Sodium: 178mg; Phosphorus: 140mg; Potassium: 186mg

Difficulty Rating: ☆ ☆

Tips: Add mushrooms or spinach for extra flavor and nutrients.

Average cost: $2.50

2. Oatmeal with Berries and Nuts

Servings: 1
Preparation time: 5 minutes
Cooking time: 5 minutes
Ingredients:

- 1/2 cup rolled oats
- 1 cup water
- 1/4 cup mixed berries (blueberries, raspberries, strawberries)
- 1 tablespoon chopped nuts (almonds, walnuts, or pecans)
- 1 teaspoon honey (optional)

Directions:

1. In a saucepan, bring the water to a boil.

2. Add the rolled oats and reduce heat to low. Cook for 3-5 minutes, stirring occasionally, until the oats are tender, and the mixture thickens.

3. Remove from heat and transfer the oatmeal to a bowl.

4. Top with mixed berries, chopped nuts, and drizzle with honey if desired.

Nutritional Values per Serving: Calories: 265 kcal; Protein: 7.3 g; Carbohydrates: 40g; Dietary Fiber: 6g; Total Fat: 8g; Saturated Fat: 1g; Cholesterol: 0mg; Sodium: 5mg; Phosphorus: 180mg; Potassium: 240mg

Difficulty Rating: ☆

Tips: Use different types of berries or switch out the nuts for seeds like chia or flaxseeds.

Average cost: $1.50

3. Greek Yogurt Parfait

Servings: 1
Preparation time: 5 minutes
Cooking time: 0 minutes
Ingredients:

- 1/2 cup plain Greek yogurt
- 1/4 cup low-sugar granola
- 1/4 cup mixed berries (blueberries, raspberries, strawberries)
- 1 tablespoon honey (optional)

Directions:

1. In a glass or bowl, layer the Greek yogurt, granola, and mixed berries.
2. Drizzle with honey if desired.

Nutritional Values per Serving: Calories: 220 kcal; Protein: 13.5 g; Carbohydrates: 25g; Dietary Fiber: 3g; Total Fat: 4g; Saturated Fat: 0g; Cholesterol: 0mg; Sodium: 50mg; Phosphorus: 100mg; Potassium: 200mg

Difficulty Rating: ☆

Tips: Add a sprinkle of cinnamon or a tablespoon of flaxseeds for extra flavor and nutrients.

Average cost: $2.00

4. Whole Wheat Pancakes

Servings: 2
Preparation time: 10 minutes
Cooking time: 10 minutes
Ingredients:

- 1 cup whole wheat flour
- 1 tablespoon baking powder
- 1/4 teaspoon salt
- 1 tablespoon honey
- 1 cup milk (or almond milk for a dairy-free option)
- 1 large egg
- Cooking spray

Directions:

1. In a mixing bowl, whisk together the whole wheat flour, baking powder, and salt.
2. In a separate bowl, whisk together the honey, milk, and egg.
3. Pour the wet ingredients into the dry ingredients and stir until just combined.
4. Heat a non-stick skillet or griddle over medium heat and spray with cooking spray.
5. Pour 1/4 cup of batter onto the skillet for each pancake and cook until bubbles form on the surface.
6. Flip and cook for another 1-2 minutes until golden brown.

Nutritional Values per Serving: Calories: 594 kcal; Protein: 30 g; Carbohydrates: 45g; Dietary Fiber: 7g; Total Fat: 5g; Saturated Fat: 1g; Cholesterol: 93mg; Sodium: 679mg; Phosphorus: 240mg; Potassium: 320mg

Difficulty Rating: ☆ ☆

Tips: Add sliced bananas or blueberries to the pancake batter for extra flavor.

Average cost: $2.50

5. Vegetable Omelette

Servings: 1
Preparation time: 5 minutes
Cooking time: 10 minutes
Ingredients:

- 2 large eggs
- 1/4 cup diced bell peppers (any color)
- 1/4 cup diced onions
- 1/4 cup diced tomatoes
- 1/4 cup chopped spinach
- Salt and pepper to taste

Directions:

1. In a bowl, whisk the eggs until well beaten.

2. Heat a non-stick skillet over medium heat and spray with cooking spray.

3. Add the diced bell peppers, onions, tomatoes, and spinach to the skillet and sauté for 2-3 minutes until softened.

4. Pour the beaten eggs into the skillet and cook, lifting the edges to allow the uncooked eggs to flow underneath.

5. Season with salt and pepper to taste.

6. Fold the omelette in half and cook for another 1-2 minutes until the eggs are cooked through.

Nutritional Values per Serving: Calories: 202 kcal; Protein: 13.8 g; Carbohydrates: 8g; Dietary Fiber: 2g; Total Fat: 10g; Saturated Fat: 3g; Cholesterol: 372mg; Sodium: 178mg; Phosphorus: 140mg; Potassium: 186mg

Difficulty Rating: ☆ ☆

Tips for ingredient variations: Add mushrooms or zucchini for extra flavor and nutrients.

Average cost: $2.00

6. Avocado Toast with Egg

Servings: 1
Preparation time: 5 minutes
Cooking time: 5 minutes
Ingredients:

- 1 slice whole wheat bread
- 1/2 ripe avocado, mashed
- 1 large egg
- Salt and pepper to taste

Directions:

1. Toast the whole wheat bread.

2. Spread the mashed avocado on the toast.

3. Heat a non-stick skillet over medium heat and spray with cooking spray.

4. Crack the egg into the skillet and cook to your desired doneness.

5. Place the cooked egg on top of the avocado toast and season with salt and pepper.

Nutritional Values per Serving: Calories: 253 kcal; Protein: 11.3 g; Carbohydrates: 20g; Dietary Fiber: 8g; Total Fat: 15g; Saturated Fat: 3g; Cholesterol: 186mg; Sodium: 160mg; Phosphorus: 140mg; Potassium: 470mg

Difficulty Rating: ☆

Tips: Add sliced tomatoes or a sprinkle of feta cheese for extra flavor.

Average cost: $2.00

7. Cottage Cheese and Fruit Bowl

Servings: 1
Preparation time: 5 minutes
Cooking time: 0 minutes
Ingredients:

- 1/2 cup low-fat cottage cheese
- 1/4 cup mixed berries (blueberries, raspberries, strawberries)
- 1/4 cup diced pineapple
- 1 tablespoon chopped nuts (almonds, walnuts, or pecans)

Directions:

1. In a bowl, combine the cottage cheese, mixed berries, diced pineapple, and chopped nuts.

Nutritional Values per Serving: Calories: 209 kcal; Protein: 15.75 g; Carbohydrates: 15g; Dietary Fiber: 3g; Total Fat: 8g; Saturated Fat: 1g; Cholesterol: 10mg; Sodium: 400mg; Phosphorus: 240mg; Potassium: 220mg

Difficulty Rating: ☆

Tips: Use different fruits based on your preference or what's in season.

Average cost: $2.50

8. Breakfast Burrito

Servings: 1
Preparation time: 5 minutes
Cooking time: 10 minutes
Ingredients:

- 1 whole wheat tortilla
- 2 large eggs, scrambled
- 1/4 cup diced bell peppers (any color)
- 1/4 cup diced onions
- 1/4 cup shredded low-fat cheese
- Salsa or hot sauce (optional)

Directions:

1. Heat a non-stick skillet over medium heat and spray with cooking spray.

2. Add the diced bell peppers and onions to the skillet and sauté for 2-3 minutes until softened.

3. Add the scrambled eggs to the skillet and cook until the eggs are cooked through.

4. Warm the whole wheat tortilla in the microwave or on a skillet.

5. Place the scrambled eggs, sautéed vegetables, shredded cheese, and salsa or hot sauce (if desired) on the tortilla.

6. Fold the sides of the tortilla over the filling and roll it up.

Nutritional Values per Serving: Calories: 324 kcal; Protein: 20.4 g; Carbohydrates: 30g; Dietary Fiber: 5g; Total Fat: 15g; Saturated Fat: 5g; Cholesterol: 372mg; Sodium: 400mg; Phosphorus: 220mg; Potassium: 260mg

Difficulty Rating: ☆ ☆

Tips: Add diced tomatoes, avocado slices, or black beans for extra flavor and nutrients.

Average cost: $3.00

9. Fruit and Yogurt Smoothie

Servings: 1
Preparation time: 5 minutes
Cooking time: 0 minutes
Ingredients:

- 1/2 cup plain Greek yogurt
- 1/2 cup mixed berries (blueberries, raspberries, strawberries)
- 1/2 banana
- 1/2 cup unsweetened almond milk (or any milk of your choice)
- 1 tablespoon honey (optional)

Directions:

1. In a blender, combine the Greek yogurt, mixed berries, banana, almond milk, and honey (if desired).
2. Blend until smooth and creamy.

Nutritional Values per Serving: Calories: 187 kcal; Protein: 11.6 g; Carbohydrates: 30g; Dietary Fiber: 5g; Total Fat: 2g; Saturated Fat: 0g; Cholesterol: 0mg; Sodium: 100mg; Phosphorus: 160mg; Potassium: 470mg

Difficulty Rating: ☆

Tips: Add a handful of spinach or kale for an extra boost of nutrients.

Average cost: $2.50

10. Veggie Breakfast Wrap

Servings: 1
Preparation time: 10 minutes
Cooking time: 5 minutes
Ingredients:

- 1 whole wheat tortilla
- 2 large eggs, scrambled
- 1/4 cup diced bell peppers (any color)
- 1/4 cup diced onions
- 1/4 cup diced tomatoes
- 1/4 cup chopped spinach
- Salt and pepper to taste

Directions:

1. Heat a non-stick skillet over medium heat and spray with cooking spray.
2. Add the diced bell peppers, onions, tomatoes, and spinach to the skillet and sauté for 2-3 minutes until softened.
3. Add the scrambled eggs to the skillet and cook until the eggs are cooked through.
4. Warm the whole wheat tortilla in the microwave or on a skillet.
5. Place the scrambled eggs and sautéed vegetables on the tortilla.
6. Season with salt and pepper to taste.
7. Fold the sides of the tortilla over the filling and roll it up.

Nutritional Values per Serving: Calories: 296 kcal; Protein: 13.8 g; Carbohydrates: 35g; Dietary Fiber: 7g; Total Fat: 10g; Saturated Fat: 3g; Cholesterol: 372mg; Sodium: 260mg; Phosphorus: 180mg; Potassium: 320mg

Difficulty Rating: ☆ ☆

Tips: Add sliced avocado or a dollop of Greek yogurt for extra creaminess.

Average cost: $2.50

CHAPTER 9: DIABETIC DIET LUNCH

Lunch is a crucial meal for individuals with diabetes, as it provides an opportunity to regulate blood sugar levels and maintain overall health. A diabetic-friendly lunch should consist of a balanced combination of carbohydrates, proteins, and healthy fats. These components work together to ensure a steady release of glucose into the bloodstream, preventing sudden spikes or drops in blood sugar levels.

Carbohydrates play a significant role in a diabetic diet, as they directly affect blood sugar levels. However, it is important to choose complex carbohydrates over simple ones. Complex carbohydrates, such as whole grains, legumes, and vegetables, are digested more slowly, resulting in a gradual increase in blood sugar levels. On the other hand, simple carbohydrates, found in sugary snacks and processed foods, can cause rapid spikes in blood sugar levels and should be avoided.

Proteins are essential for building and repairing tissues, as well as regulating blood sugar levels. Including lean sources of protein in a diabetic lunch can help stabilize blood sugar levels and keep you feeling full for longer. Good sources of protein include skinless poultry, fish, tofu, beans, and low-fat dairy products.

Healthy fats are also an important component of a diabetic-friendly lunch. These fats help improve heart health and promote satiety. Incorporating sources of healthy fats, such as avocados, nuts, seeds, and olive oil, can provide essential nutrients and help maintain stable blood sugar levels.

In addition to choosing the right ingredients, portion control is crucial for managing diabetes. It is important to be mindful of the quantity of food consumed during lunchtime. Balancing the amount of carbohydrates, proteins, and fats is essential in maintaining a healthy blood sugar level.

CHAPTER 10: AFFORDABLE LUNCH RECIPES

11. Chicken and Vegetable Stir-Fry

Servings: 2
Preparation time: 10 minutes
Cooking time: 15 minutes
Ingredients:
- 1 boneless, skinless chicken breast, sliced
- 1 cup mixed vegetables (broccoli, bell peppers, carrots)
- 2 cloves garlic, minced
- 1 tablespoon low-sodium soy sauce
- 1 teaspoon sesame oil
- 1/2 teaspoon ginger, grated
- Salt and pepper to taste

Directions:
1. Heat sesame oil in a pan over medium heat.
2. Add minced garlic and grated ginger, sauté for a minute.
3. Add sliced chicken breast and cook until no longer pink.
4. Add mixed vegetables and cook until tender-crisp.
5. Stir in low-sodium soy sauce, salt, and pepper.
6. Serve hot with a side of brown rice or quinoa.

Nutritional Values per Serving: Calories: 405 kcal; Protein: 49.8 g; Carbohydrates: 15g; Dietary Fiber: 4g; Total Fat: 5g; Saturated Fat: 1g; Cholesterol: 45mg; Sodium: 300mg; Phosphorus: 200mg; Potassium: 400mg

Difficulty Rating: ☆ ☆

Tips: You can add other vegetables like snap peas or mushrooms for more variety. For a renal diet variation, reduce the amount of soy sauce or use a low-sodium alternative.

12. Turkey and Avocado Wrap

Servings: 1
Preparation time: 5 minutes
Cooking time: N/A
Ingredients:
- 2 slices of low-sodium turkey breast
- 1/4 avocado, sliced
- 1 whole wheat tortilla
- 1 tablespoon Greek yogurt
- 1/2 cup mixed greens
- Salt and pepper to taste

Directions:
1. Lay the whole wheat tortilla flat on a clean surface.
2. Spread Greek yogurt evenly on the tortilla.
3. Layer turkey slices, avocado slices, and mixed greens on top.
4. Season with salt and pepper.
5. Roll the tortilla tightly, tucking in the sides as you go.
6. Slice in half and serve.

Nutritional Values per Serving: Calories: 351 kcal; Protein: 24.4 g; Carbohydrates: 30g; Dietary Fiber: 8g; Total Fat: 10g; Saturated Fat: 2g; Cholesterol: 25mg; Sodium: 200mg; Phosphorus: 150mg; Potassium: 350mg

Difficulty Rating: ☆

Tips: You can add other vegetables like sliced cucumbers or tomatoes for extra crunch and flavor. For a renal diet variation, use low-sodium turkey breast slices and limit the amount of added salt.

13. Tuna Salad Lettuce Wraps

Servings: 2
Preparation time: 10 minutes
Cooking time: N/A
Ingredients:

- 1 can of tuna in water, drained
- 2 tablespoons mayonnaise (low-fat or light)
- 1 tablespoon Dijon mustard
- 1 celery stalk, diced
- 1/4 red onion, diced
- Salt and pepper to taste
- 4 large lettuce leaves

Directions:

1. In a bowl, combine tuna, mayonnaise, Dijon mustard, diced celery, and red onion.
2. Mix well until all ingredients are evenly incorporated.
3. Season with salt and pepper.
4. Spoon the tuna salad onto the lettuce leaves.
5. Wrap the lettuce leaves around the filling, securing with toothpicks if necessary.
6. Serve chilled.

Nutritional Values per Serving: Calories: 211 kcal; Protein: 22.8 g; Carbohydrates: 5g; Dietary Fiber: 2g; Total Fat: 8g; Saturated Fat: 1g; Cholesterol: 20mg; Sodium: 300mg; Phosphorus: 150mg; Potassium: 250mg

Difficulty Rating: ☆ ☆

Tips: You can add diced pickles or cherry tomatoes to the tuna salad for added flavor and texture. For a renal diet variation, use low-sodium tuna and limit the amount of added salt.

14. Lentil and Vegetable Soup

Servings: 4
Preparation time: 10 minutes
Cooking time: 30 minutes
Ingredients:

- 1 cup dried lentils, rinsed and drained
- 1 onion, diced
- 2 carrots, diced
- 2 celery stalks, diced
- 2 cloves garlic, minced
- 4 cups low-sodium vegetable broth
- 1 teaspoon cumin
- 1/2 teaspoon paprika
- Salt and pepper to taste

Directions:

1. In a large pot, sauté onion, carrots, celery, and garlic until softened.
2. Add lentils, vegetable broth, cumin, and paprika.
3. Bring to a boil, then reduce heat and simmer for 25-30 minutes until lentils are tender.
4. Season with salt and pepper.
5. Serve hot.

Nutritional Values per Serving: Calories: 363 kcal; Protein: 19 g; Carbohydrates: 30g; Dietary Fiber: 12g; Total Fat: 1g; Saturated Fat: 0g; Cholesterol: 0mg; Sodium: 200mg; Phosphorus: 250mg; Potassium: 600mg

Difficulty Rating: ☆ ☆

Tips: You can add other vegetables like zucchini or spinach for added nutrition. For a renal diet variation, limit the amount of added salt and use low-sodium vegetable broth.

15. Quinoa and Vegetable Salad

Servings: 2
Preparation time: 15 minutes
Cooking time: 15 minutes
Ingredients:

- 1/2 cup quinoa, rinsed
- 1 cup water
- 1/2 cucumber, diced
- 1/2 bell pepper, diced
- 1/4 red onion, diced
- 1/4 cup cherry tomatoes, halved
- 2 tablespoons lemon juice
- 1 tablespoon olive oil
- Salt and pepper to taste

Directions:

1. In a saucepan, bring water to a boil.

2. Add quinoa, reduce heat, cover, and simmer for 15 minutes until water is absorbed and quinoa is tender.

3. In a bowl, combine cooked quinoa, cucumber, bell pepper, red onion, and cherry tomatoes.

4. In a separate small bowl, whisk together lemon juice, olive oil, salt, and pepper.

5. Pour the dressing over the quinoa and vegetable mixture, tossing to coat evenly.

6. Serve chilled or at room temperature.

Nutritional Values per Serving: Calories: 425 kcal; Protein: 10.1 g; Carbohydrates: 35g; Dietary Fiber: 6g; Total Fat: 6g; Saturated Fat: 1g; Cholesterol: 0mg; Sodium: 100mg; Phosphorus: 200mg; Potassium: 400mg

Difficulty Rating: ☆

Tips: You can add chopped fresh herbs like parsley or basil for extra flavor. For a renal diet variation, use low-sodium vegetable broth to cook the quinoa and limit the amount of added salt.

16. Spinach and Mushroom Omelette

Servings: 1
Preparation time: 5 minutes
Cooking time: 10 minutes
Ingredients:

- 2 eggs
- 1 cup fresh spinach leaves
- 4-5 button mushrooms, sliced
- 1/4 onion, diced
- 1 tablespoon olive oil
- Salt and pepper to taste

Directions:

1. In a bowl, whisk the eggs until well beaten.

2. Heat olive oil in a non-stick skillet over medium heat.

3. Add diced onion and sliced mushrooms, sauté until softened.

4. Add fresh spinach leaves and cook until wilted.

5. Pour the beaten eggs over the vegetables, spreading them evenly.

6. Cook until the omelette is set, then flip and cook for another minute.

7. Season with salt and pepper.

8. Serve hot.

Nutritional Values per Serving: Calories: 306 kcal; Protein: 15 g; Carbohydrates: 8g; Dietary Fiber: 2g; Total Fat: 15g; Saturated Fat: 3g; Cholesterol: 370mg; Sodium: 200mg; Phosphorus: 250mg; Potassium: 400mg

Difficulty Rating: ☆ ☆

Tips: You can add low-fat cheese or diced tomatoes for added flavor. For a renal diet variation, limit the amount of added salt and use a non-stick skillet to reduce the need for oil.

17. Black Bean and Vegetable Quesadilla

Servings: 2
Preparation time: 10 minutes
Cooking time: 10 minutes
Ingredients:

- 4 small whole wheat tortillas
- 1/2 cup black beans, rinsed and drained
- 1/4 cup corn kernels
- 1/4 cup diced bell peppers
- 1/4 cup shredded low-fat cheese
- 1/4 teaspoon cumin
- 1/4 teaspoon chili powder
- Salt and pepper to taste

Directions:

1. Lay two tortillas flat on a clean surface.
2. Divide black beans, corn kernels, diced bell peppers, and shredded cheese evenly between the two tortillas.
3. Sprinkle with cumin, chili powder, salt, and pepper.
4. Top with the remaining two tortillas.
5. Heat a non-stick skillet over medium heat.
6. Cook each quesadilla for 2-3 minutes on each side until cheese is melted, and tortillas are crispy.
7. Slice into wedges and serve hot.

Nutritional Values per Serving:

Calories: 650 kcal; Protein: 23.7 g; Carbohydrates: 35g; Dietary Fiber: 8g; Total Fat: 6g; Saturated Fat: 2g; Cholesterol: 10mg; Sodium: 300mg; Phosphorus: 200mg; Potassium: 400mg

Difficulty Rating: ☆

Tips: You can add sliced avocado or diced tomatoes as a topping. For a renal diet variation, use low-sodium black beans and limit the amount of added salt.

18. Greek Salad with Grilled Chicken

Servings: 2
Preparation time: 15 minutes
Cooking time: 15 minutes
Ingredients:

- 2 boneless, skinless chicken breasts
- 2 cups mixed salad greens
- 1/2 cucumber, diced
- 1/2 bell pepper, diced
- 1/4 red onion, thinly sliced
- 1/4 cup Kalamata olives
- 1/4 cup crumbled feta cheese
- 2 tablespoons lemon juice
- 1 tablespoon olive oil
- Salt and pepper to taste

Directions:

1. Preheat a grill or grill pan over medium-high heat.
2. Season chicken breasts with salt and pepper.
3. Grill chicken for 6-8 minutes per side until cooked through.
4. Let the chicken rest for a few minutes, then slice into thin strips.
5. In a large bowl, combine mixed salad greens, diced cucumber, diced bell pepper, thinly sliced red onion, Kalamata olives, and crumbled feta cheese.
6. In a separate small bowl, whisk together lemon juice, olive oil, salt, and pepper.
7. Pour the dressing over the salad mixture, tossing to coat evenly.
8. Top the salad with grilled chicken slices.
9. Serve chilled.

Nutritional Values per Serving:

Calories: 584 kcal; Protein: 67.6 g; Carbohydrates: 10g; Dietary Fiber: 3g; Total Fat: 15g; Saturated Fat: 5g; Cholesterol: 80mg; Sodium: 400mg; Phosphorus: 250mg; Potassium: 600mg

Difficulty Rating: ☆ ☆

Tips: You can add cherry tomatoes or sliced avocado for extra flavor. For a renal diet variation, use low-sodium feta cheese and limit the amount of added salt.

19. Salmon and Asparagus Foil Packets

Servings: 2
Preparation time: 10 minutes
Cooking time: 20 minutes
Ingredients:

- 2 salmon fillets
- 1 bunch asparagus, trimmed
- 1 lemon, sliced
- 2 cloves garlic, minced
- 1 tablespoon olive oil
- Salt and pepper to taste

Directions:

1. Preheat the oven to 400°F (200°C).

2. Cut two large pieces of aluminum foil.

3. Place a salmon fillet on each piece of foil.

4. Arrange asparagus spears and lemon slices around the salmon.

5. Drizzle with olive oil and sprinkle minced garlic, salt, and pepper.

6. Fold the foil over the salmon and vegetables, sealing the edges tightly.

7. Place the foil packets on a baking sheet and bake for 15-20 minutes until salmon is cooked through.

8. Serve hot.

Nutritional Values per Serving:

Calories: 601 kcal; Protein: 46.4 g; Carbohydrates: 10g; Dietary Fiber: 4g; Total Fat: 15g; Saturated Fat: 2g; Cholesterol: 70mg; Sodium: 200mg; Phosphorus: 350mg; Potassium: 800mg

Difficulty Rating: ☆ ☆

Tips: You can add sliced cherry tomatoes or sprinkle fresh dill on top before baking. For a renal diet variation, limit the amount of added salt.

20. Veggie and Hummus Wrap

Servings: 1
Preparation time: 5 minutes
Cooking time: N/A
Ingredients:

- 1 whole wheat tortilla
- 2 tablespoons hummus
- 1/4 cucumber, sliced
- 1/4 bell pepper, sliced
- 1/4 carrot, julienned
- 1/4 cup mixed salad greens
- Salt and pepper to taste

Directions:

1. Lay the whole wheat tortilla flat on a clean surface.

2. Spread hummus evenly on the tortilla.

3. Layer cucumber slices, bell pepper slices, julienned carrot, and mixed salad greens on top.

4. Season with salt and pepper.

5. Roll the tortilla tightly, tucking in the sides as you go.

6. Slice in half and serve.

Nutritional Values per Serving: Calories: 241 kcal; Protein: 9.6 g; Carbohydrates: 35g; Dietary Fiber: 8g; Total Fat: 6g; Saturated Fat: 1g; Cholesterol: 0mg; Sodium: 300mg; Phosphorus: 150mg; Potassium: 400mg

Difficulty Rating: ☆

Tips: You can add sliced avocado or sprinkle with lemon juice for extra flavor. For a renal diet variation, use low-sodium hummus and limit the amount of added salt.

CHAPTER 11: DIABETIC DIET DINNER

When planning a diabetic diet dinner, it is important to consider the role of different nutrients. Carbohydrates, proteins, and fats all have distinct impacts on blood sugar levels, and understanding their effects is key to creating a well-rounded meal.

Carbohydrates are the primary source of energy for the body. However, for diabetics, it is important to choose carbohydrates that have a low glycemic index (GI) to prevent spikes in blood sugar levels. Whole grains, legumes, and non-starchy vegetables are excellent choices as they provide fiber, vitamins, and minerals while being slowly digested, resulting in a gradual release of glucose into the bloodstream.

Proteins are essential for repairing and building tissues. Including lean sources of protein such as poultry, fish, tofu, or legumes in a diabetic dinner can help control blood sugar levels. These proteins are low in saturated fats and provide essential amino acids necessary for maintaining a healthy body.

Fats, although often demonized, are an important part of a balanced diet. However, it is crucial to choose healthy fats such as avocados, nuts, seeds, and olive oil. These fats provide vital nutrients and can help improve insulin sensitivity, reducing the risk of complications associated with diabetes.

In addition to considering the role of different nutrients, there are specific food suggestions that can be incorporated into a diabetic-friendly dinner. A well-rounded meal might include grilled chicken breast with a side of roasted vegetables, a small portion of quinoa or brown rice, and a fresh salad dressed with olive oil and vinegar. This combination provides a balance of proteins, healthy carbohydrates, and fats.

It is equally important to avoid certain foods that can negatively impact blood sugar levels. Processed foods, sugary beverages, refined grains, and high-fat dairy products should be limited or eliminated from a diabetic dinner. These foods can cause rapid spikes in blood sugar levels and contribute to weight gain, which can worsen diabetes symptoms.

CHAPTER 12: AFFORDABLE DINNER RECIPES

21. Grilled Lemon Herb Chicken Breast

Servings: 4
Preparation time: 10 minutes
Cooking time: 15 minutes
Ingredients:
- 4 boneless, skinless chicken breasts
- 2 tablespoons olive oil
- 1 tablespoon lemon juice
- 1 teaspoon dried thyme
- 1 teaspoon dried rosemary
- Salt and pepper to taste

Directions:

1. Preheat the grill to medium-high heat.

2. In a small bowl, mix together the olive oil, lemon juice, thyme, rosemary, salt, and pepper.

3. Brush the chicken breasts with the herb mixture.

4. Grill the chicken for about 6-8 minutes per side, or until cooked through.

5. Serve hot with a side of steamed vegetables.

Nutritional Values per Serving: Calories: 828 kcal; Protein: 124 g; Carbohydrates: 0g; Dietary Fiber: 0g; Total Fat: 9g; Saturated Fat: 2g; Cholesterol: 86mg; Sodium: 67mg; Phosphorus: 215mg; Potassium: 296mg

Difficulty Rating: ☆ ☆

Tips: For a renal diet variation, reduce the amount of salt used in the marinade.

22. Baked Salmon with Dill Sauce

Servings: 2
Preparation time: 5 minutes
Cooking time: 15 minutes
Ingredients:
- 2 salmon fillets
- 2 tablespoons lemon juice
- 1 tablespoon fresh dill, chopped
- 1 clove garlic, minced
- Salt and pepper to taste

Directions:

1. Preheat the oven to 400°F (200°C).

2. Place the salmon fillets on a baking sheet lined with parchment paper.

3. In a small bowl, mix together the lemon juice, dill, garlic, salt, and pepper.

4. Brush the dill sauce over the salmon fillets.

5. Bake for 12-15 minutes, or until the salmon is cooked through and flakes easily with a fork.

6. Serve hot with a side of roasted asparagus.

Nutritional Values per Serving: Calories: 504 kcal; Protein: 44 g; Carbohydrates: 1g; Dietary Fiber: 0g; Total Fat: 21g; Saturated Fat: 5g; Cholesterol: 62mg; Sodium: 73mg; Phosphorus: 249mg; Potassium: 534mg

Difficulty Rating: ☆ ☆ ☆

Tips: For a renal diet variation, use low-sodium soy sauce instead of salt in the dill sauce.

23. Turkey and Vegetable Stir-Fry

Servings: 4
Preparation time: 15 minutes
Cooking time: 15 minutes
Ingredients:

- 1 pound turkey breast, cut into thin strips
- 2 tablespoons low-sodium soy sauce
- 1 tablespoon sesame oil
- 1 teaspoon ginger, grated
- 2 cloves garlic, minced
- 2 cups mixed vegetables (broccoli, bell peppers, carrots, snap peas)
- Salt and pepper to taste

Directions:

1. In a bowl, combine the turkey strips, soy sauce, sesame oil, ginger, and garlic. Let it marinate for 10 minutes.

2. Heat a large skillet or wok over medium-high heat. Add the marinated turkey and cook until browned.

3. Add the mixed vegetables to the skillet and stir-fry for 5-7 minutes, or until crisp-tender.

4. Season with salt and pepper to taste.

5. Serve hot with a side of brown rice.

Nutritional Values per Serving: Calories: 360 kcal; Protein: 35 g; Carbohydrates: 8g; Dietary Fiber: 2g; Total Fat: 4g; Saturated Fat: 1g; Cholesterol: 62mg; Sodium: 304mg; Phosphorus: 255mg; Potassium: 528mg

Difficulty Rating: ☆☆☆

Tips: For a renal diet variation, use low-sodium soy sauce, and limit the amount of salt added.

24. Quinoa and Black Bean Salad

Servings: 6
Preparation time: 15 minutes
Cooking time: 20 minutes
Ingredients:

- 1 cup quinoa, rinsed
- 2 cups water
- 1 can (15 ounces) black beans, rinsed and drained
- 1 cup cherry tomatoes, halved
- 1/2 cup red onion, finely chopped
- 1/4 cup fresh cilantro, chopped
- 2 tablespoons lime juice
- 2 tablespoons olive oil
- Salt and pepper to taste

Directions:

1. In a medium saucepan, bring the water to a boil. Add the quinoa and reduce heat to low. Cover and simmer for 15-20 minutes, or until the quinoa is tender and the water is absorbed.

2. In a large bowl, combine the cooked quinoa, black beans, cherry tomatoes, red onion, and cilantro.

3. In a small bowl, whisk together the lime juice, olive oil, salt, and pepper. Pour the dressing over the quinoa mixture and toss to combine.

4. Serve chilled as a refreshing salad.

Nutritional Values per Serving: Calories: 1864 kcal; Protein: 31 g; Carbohydrates: 30g; Dietary Fiber: 7g; Total Fat: 6g; Saturated Fat: 1g; Cholesterol: 0mg; Sodium: 196mg; Phosphorus: 218mg; Potassium: 491mg

Difficulty Rating: ☆☆

Tips: For a renal diet variation, rinse the canned black beans thoroughly to remove excess sodium.

25. Vegetable Curry with Brown Rice

Servings: 4
Preparation time: 10 minutes
Cooking time: 25 minutes
Ingredients:

- 1 tablespoon olive oil
- 1 onion, chopped
- 2 cloves garlic, minced
- 1 tablespoon curry powder
- 1 teaspoon ground cumin
- 1/2 teaspoon ground turmeric
- 1 can (14 ounces) diced tomatoes
- 1 can (14 ounces) coconut milk
- 2 cups mixed vegetables (cauliflower, carrots, peas, bell peppers)
- Salt and pepper to taste
- 2 cups cooked brown rice

Directions:

1. Heat the olive oil in a large skillet over medium heat. Add the onion and garlic and cook until softened.

2. Stir in the curry powder, cumin, and turmeric. Cook for an additional minute.

3. Add the diced tomatoes (with their juice) and coconut milk to the skillet. Bring to a simmer.

4. Add the mixed vegetables and season with salt and pepper. Cook for 10-15 minutes, or until the vegetables are tender.

5. Serve the vegetable curry over cooked brown rice.

Nutritional Values per Serving: Calories: 514 kcal; Protein: 13 g; Carbohydrates: 50g; Dietary Fiber: 8g; Total Fat: 19g; Saturated Fat: 14g; Cholesterol: 0mg; Sodium: 259mg; Phosphorus: 241mg; Potassium: 780mg

Difficulty Rating: ☆ ☆ ☆

Tips: For a renal diet variation, use low-sodium diced tomatoes and limit the amount of salt added.

26. Spinach and Feta Stuffed Chicken Breast

Servings: 2
Preparation time: 15 minutes
Cooking time: 25 minutes
Ingredients:

- 2 boneless, skinless chicken breasts
- 2 cups fresh spinach, chopped
- 1/4 cup crumbled feta cheese
- 1 clove garlic, minced
- Salt and pepper to taste

Directions:

1. Preheat the oven to 375°F (190°C).

2. Cut a slit lengthwise through each chicken breast to create a pocket.

3. In a bowl, combine the chopped spinach, feta cheese, garlic, salt, and pepper.

4. Stuff each chicken breast with the spinach and feta mixture, pressing the edges to seal.

5. Place the stuffed chicken breasts on a baking sheet lined with parchment paper.

6. Bake for 20-25 minutes, or until the chicken is cooked through.

7. Serve hot with a side of roasted sweet potatoes.

Nutritional Values per Serving: Calories: 444 kcal; Protein: 66.9 g; Carbohydrates: 2g; Dietary Fiber: 1g; Total Fat: 9g; Saturated Fat: 4g; Cholesterol: 86mg; Sodium: 214mg; Phosphorus: 245mg; Potassium: 441mg

Difficulty Rating: ☆ ☆ ☆

Tips: For a renal diet variation, use low-sodium feta cheese and limit the amount of salt added.

27. Lentil and Vegetable Soup

Servings: 6
Preparation time: 10 minutes
Cooking time: 30 minutes
Ingredients:
- 1 tablespoon olive oil
- 1 onion, chopped
- 2 carrots, diced
- 2 stalks celery, diced
- 2 cloves garlic, minced
- 1 cup dried lentils
- 4 cups low-sodium vegetable broth
- 1 can (14 ounces) diced tomatoes
- 2 cups chopped kale
- Salt and pepper to taste

Directions:

1. Heat the olive oil in a large pot over medium heat. Add the onion, carrots, celery, and garlic. Cook until the vegetables are softened.

2. Add the dried lentils, vegetable broth, and diced tomatoes to the pot. Bring to a boil, then reduce heat to low and simmer for 20-25 minutes, or until the lentils are tender.

3. Stir in the chopped kale and cook for an additional 5 minutes, or until wilted.

4. Season with salt and pepper to taste.

5. Serve hot as a comforting soup.

Nutritional Values per Serving: Calories: 1963 kcal; Protein: 24 g; Carbohydrates: 30g; Dietary Fiber: 12g; Total Fat: 3g; Saturated Fat: 0g; Cholesterol: 0mg; Sodium: 197mg; Phosphorus: 232mg; Potassium: 847mg

Difficulty Rating: ☆ ☆

Tips: For a renal diet variation, use low-sodium vegetable broth and limit the amount of salt added.

28. Shrimp and Broccoli Stir-Fry

Servings: 2
Preparation time: 10 minutes
Cooking time: 10 minutes
Ingredients:
- 1 tablespoon olive oil
- 1/2 pound shrimp, peeled and deveined
- 2 cups broccoli florets
- 1 bell pepper, sliced
- 2 cloves garlic, minced
- 2 tablespoons low-sodium soy sauce
- 1 tablespoon rice vinegar
- 1/2 teaspoon ginger, grated
- Salt and pepper to taste

Directions:

1. Heat the olive oil in a large skillet or wok over medium-high heat. Add the shrimp and cook until pink and cooked through. Remove from the skillet and set aside.

2. In the same skillet, add the broccoli florets, bell pepper, and garlic. Stir-fry for 5-7 minutes, or until the vegetables are crisp-tender.

3. In a small bowl, whisk together the soy sauce, rice vinegar, ginger, salt, and pepper. Pour the sauce over the vegetables and stir to coat.

4. Add the cooked shrimp back to the skillet and cook for an additional 2 minutes, or until heated through.

5. Serve hot with a side of brown rice.

Nutritional Values per Serving: Calories: 287 kcal; Protein: 26.6 g; Carbohydrates: 11g; Dietary Fiber: 4g; Total Fat: 8g; Saturated Fat: 1g; Cholesterol: 143mg; Sodium: 501mg; Phosphorus: 217mg; Potassium: 527mg

Difficulty Rating: ☆ ☆

Tips: For a renal diet variation, use low-sodium soy sauce and limit the amount of salt added.

29. Eggplant Parmesan

Servings: 4
Preparation time: 15 minutes
Cooking time: 30 minutes
Ingredients:

- 1 large eggplant, sliced into rounds
- 1 cup whole wheat breadcrumbs
- 1/2 cup grated Parmesan cheese
- 2 eggs, beaten
- 2 cups marinara sauce
- 1 cup shredded mozzarella cheese
- Salt and pepper to taste

Directions:

1. Preheat the oven to 375°F (190°C).
2. Season the eggplant slices with salt and pepper. Let them sit for 10 minutes to remove excess moisture, then pat dry with a paper towel.
3. In a shallow dish, combine the breadcrumbs and Parmesan cheese.
4. Dip each eggplant slice into the beaten eggs, then coat with the breadcrumb mixture.
5. Place the coated eggplant slices on a baking sheet lined with parchment paper.
6. Bake for 15 minutes, or until the eggplant is tender, and the breadcrumbs are golden.
7. Spread a thin layer of marinara sauce on the bottom of a baking dish. Arrange half of the baked eggplant slices on top.
8. Top with another layer of marinara sauce and sprinkle with half of the shredded mozzarella cheese.
9. Repeat the layers with the remaining eggplant slices, marinara sauce, and mozzarella cheese.
10. Bake for 15 minutes, or until the cheese is melted and bubbly.
11. Serve hot as a delicious vegetarian dinner.

Nutritional Values per Serving: Calories: 1135 kcal; Protein: 51.2 g; Carbohydrates: 32g; Dietary Fiber: 8g; Total Fat: 15g; Saturated Fat: 7g; Cholesterol: 112mg; Sodium: 898mg; Phosphorus: 312mg; Potassium: 614mg

Difficulty Rating: ☆ ☆ ☆

Tips: For a renal diet variation, use low-sodium marinara sauce and limit the amount of salt added.

30. Greek Salad with Grilled Chicken

Servings: 2
Preparation time: 15 minutes
Cooking time: 15 minutes
Ingredients:

- 2 boneless, skinless chicken breasts
- 2 tablespoons lemon juice
- 2 tablespoons olive oil
- 1 teaspoon dried oregano
- Salt and pepper to taste
- 2 cups mixed salad greens
- 1/2 cup cherry tomatoes, halved
- 1/4 cup cucumber, diced
- 1/4 cup red onion, thinly sliced
- 1/4 cup Kalamata olives
- 1/4 cup crumbled feta cheese
- 2 tablespoons Greek dressing

Directions:

1. Preheat the grill to medium-high heat.
2. In a small bowl, whisk together the lemon juice, olive oil, dried oregano, salt, and pepper.
3. Brush the chicken breasts with the marinade.
4. Grill the chicken for about 6-8 minutes per side, or until cooked through.
5. Let the chicken rest for a few minutes, then slice into strips.
6. In a large bowl, combine the mixed salad greens, cherry tomatoes, cucumber, red onion, Kalamata olives, and crumbled feta cheese.
7. Drizzle with the Greek dressing and toss to coat.
8. Top the salad with the grilled chicken slices.
9. Serve chilled as a refreshing and protein-packed dinner.

Nutritional Values per Serving: Calories: 666 kcal; Protein: 66 g; Carbohydrates: 9g; Dietary Fiber: 2g; Total Fat: 21g; Saturated Fat: 6g; Cholesterol: 86mg; Sodium: 454mg; Phosphorus: 266mg; Potassium: 518mg

Difficulty Rating: ☆ ☆

Tips: For a renal diet variation, use low-sodium Greek dressing and limit the amount of salt added.

CHAPTER 13: DIABETIC DIET SNACKS

One of the key reasons why snacks are important for people with diabetes is their ability to prevent blood sugar spikes. When there is a long gap between meals, blood sugar levels can drop too low, leading to hypoglycemia. On the other hand, consuming large meals can cause blood sugar levels to rise rapidly, resulting in hyperglycemia. Snacks help maintain a steady supply of glucose to the body, preventing these extreme fluctuations.

When selecting ingredients for diabetic snacks, it is essential to focus on those that have a low glycemic index (GI). The glycemic index measures how quickly a carbohydrate-containing food raises blood sugar levels. Foods with a low GI release glucose slowly into the bloodstream, preventing sudden spikes. Some examples of low GI ingredients that can be incorporated into diabetic snacks include whole grains, legumes, non-starchy vegetables, and lean proteins.

Whole grains, such as oats, quinoa, and brown rice, are excellent choices for diabetic snacks. They are rich in fiber, which helps regulate blood sugar levels and keeps you feeling full for longer. Additionally, the fiber content aids in maintaining a healthy weight, which is important for managing diabetes.

Legumes, such as chickpeas, lentils, and kidney beans, are another fantastic option for diabetic snacks. They are packed with protein and fiber, making them a great choice for stabilizing blood sugar levels. Legumes also have a low glycemic index, making them an ideal ingredient in diabetic-friendly snacks.

Non-starchy vegetables, such as broccoli, spinach, and bell peppers, are not only low in carbohydrates but also high in essential nutrients. These vegetables can be enjoyed raw or lightly cooked and make for a nutritious addition to any diabetic snack. Their high fiber content helps slow down the absorption of glucose, preventing blood sugar spikes.

Including lean proteins in diabetic snacks can also be beneficial. Proteins, such as skinless chicken, turkey, tofu, and Greek yogurt, help in maintaining satiety and stabilizing blood sugar levels. They also aid in building and repairing tissues, making them an important component of a balanced diabetic diet.

In addition to these ingredients, it is important to be mindful of portion sizes when consuming snacks. While snacks can be a valuable part of managing diabetes, overeating can still lead to weight gain and blood sugar imbalances. It is recommended to consult with a healthcare professional or a registered dietitian to determine the appropriate portion sizes for your individual needs.

31. Roasted Chickpeas

Servings: 4
Preparation time: 5 minutes
Cooking time: 25 minutes
Ingredients:
- 2 cans of chickpeas, drained and rinsed
- 1 tablespoon olive oil
- 1 teaspoon paprika
- 1/2 teaspoon garlic powder
- 1/2 teaspoon cumin
- Salt to taste

Directions:
1. Preheat the oven to 400°F (200°C).
2. In a bowl, toss the chickpeas with olive oil, paprika, garlic powder, cumin, and salt.
3. Spread the chickpeas in a single layer on a baking sheet.
4. Roast in the oven for 20-25 minutes, or until crispy, stirring once halfway through.

Nutritional Values per Serving: Calories: 238 kcal; Protein: 116 g; Carbohydrates: 22g; Dietary Fiber: 5g; Total Fat: 5g; Saturated Fat: 1g; Cholesterol: 0mg; Sodium: 150mg; Phosphorus: 70mg; Potassium: 250mg

Difficulty Rating: ☆ ☆

Tips: Add a pinch of cayenne pepper for a spicy kick.

32. Greek Yogurt Parfait

Servings: 1
Preparation time: 5 minutes
Ingredients:
- 1/2 cup plain Greek yogurt
- 1/4 cup fresh berries (such as strawberries, blueberries, or raspberries)
- 1 tablespoon chopped nuts (such as almonds or walnuts)
- 1 teaspoon honey (optional)

Directions:
1. In a glass or bowl, layer the Greek yogurt, fresh berries, and chopped nuts.
2. Drizzle with honey, if desired.

Nutritional Values per Serving: Calories: 109 kcal; Protein: 11.75 g; Carbohydrates: 15g; Dietary Fiber: 2g; Total Fat: 6g; Saturated Fat: 1g; Cholesterol: 5mg; Sodium: 25mg; Phosphorus: 150mg; Potassium: 200mg

Difficulty Rating: ☆

Tips: Use frozen berries if fresh ones are not available.

33. Veggie Sticks with Hummus

Servings: 2
Preparation time: 10 minutes
Ingredients:

- 2 medium carrots, cut into sticks
- 2 medium cucumbers, cut into sticks
- 1/2 cup hummus

Directions:

1. Arrange the carrot and cucumber sticks on a plate.
2. Serve with hummus for dipping.

Nutritional Values per Serving: Calories: 207 kcal; Protein: 7.4 g; Carbohydrates: 15g; Dietary Fiber: 6g; Total Fat: 10g; Saturated Fat: 1g; Cholesterol: 0mg; Sodium: 200mg; Phosphorus: 100mg; Potassium: 400mg

Difficulty Rating: ☆

Tips: Try using different vegetables like bell peppers or celery.

34. Baked Sweet Potato Chips

Servings: 2
Preparation time: 10 minutes
Cooking time: 25 minutes
Ingredients:

- 2 medium sweet potatoes, thinly sliced
- 1 tablespoon olive oil
- 1/2 teaspoon paprika
- 1/4 teaspoon garlic powder
- Salt to taste

Directions:

1. Preheat the oven to 400°F (200°C).
2. In a bowl, toss the sweet potato slices with olive oil, paprika, garlic powder, and salt.
3. Arrange the slices in a single layer on a baking sheet.
4. Bake for 20-25 minutes, or until crispy, flipping once halfway through.

Nutritional Values per Serving: Calories: 576 kcal; Protein: 8 g; Carbohydrates: 20g; Dietary Fiber: 3g; Total Fat: 5g; Saturated Fat: 1g; Cholesterol: 0mg; Sodium: 100mg; Phosphorus: 80mg; Potassium: 400mg

Difficulty Rating: ☆ ☆

Tips: Sprinkle with a pinch of cinnamon for a sweet twist.

35. Tuna Salad Lettuce Wraps

Servings: 2
Preparation time: 10 minutes
Ingredients:
- 1 can tuna, drained
- 2 tablespoons mayonnaise
- 1 tablespoon diced celery
- 1 tablespoon diced red onion
- Salt and pepper to taste
- 4 large lettuce leaves

Directions:
1. In a bowl, mix together the tuna, mayonnaise, celery, red onion, salt, and pepper.
2. Spoon the tuna salad onto the lettuce leaves.
3. Roll up the lettuce leaves to form wraps.

Nutritional Values per Serving: Calories: 446 kcal; Protein: 44.4 g; Carbohydrates: 4g; Dietary Fiber: 1g; Total Fat: 10g; Saturated Fat: 2g; Cholesterol: 25mg; Sodium: 300mg; Phosphorus: 150mg; Potassium: 200mg

Difficulty Rating: ☆ ☆

Tips: Add chopped pickles or olives for extra flavor.

36. Apple Slices with Peanut Butter

Servings: 2
Preparation time: 5 minutes
Ingredients:
- 1 medium apple, sliced
- 2 tablespoons peanut butter

Directions:
1. Arrange the apple slices on a plate.
2. Serve with peanut butter for dipping.

Nutritional Values per Serving: Calories: 387 kcal; Protein: 9 g; Carbohydrates: 20g; Dietary Fiber: 4g; Total Fat: 10g; Saturated Fat: 2g; Cholesterol: 0mg; Sodium: 100mg; Phosphorus: 100mg; Potassium: 200mg

Difficulty Rating: ☆

Tips: Use almond butter or sunflower seed butter as an alternative.

37. Cottage Cheese and Berries

Servings: 1
Preparation time: 5 minutes
Ingredients:
- 1/2 cup low-fat cottage cheese
- 1/4 cup fresh berries (such as strawberries, blueberries, or raspberries)
- **Directions:**

1. In a bowl, combine the cottage cheese and fresh berries.

Nutritional Values per Serving: Calories: 116 kcal; Protein: 14.5 g; Carbohydrates: 10g; Dietary Fiber: 2g; Total Fat: 2g; Saturated Fat: 1g; Cholesterol: 10mg; Sodium: 200mg; Phosphorus: 150mg; Potassium: 200mg

Difficulty Rating: ☆

Tips: Sprinkle with a dash of cinnamon for added flavor.

38. Mini Caprese Skewers

Servings: 4
Preparation time: 10 minutes
Ingredients:
- 8 cherry tomatoes
- 8 small mozzarella balls
- 8 small basil leaves
- 1 tablespoon balsamic glaze

Directions:

1. Thread a cherry tomato, mozzarella ball, and basil leaf onto a skewer.
2. Repeat with the remaining ingredients.
3. Drizzle with balsamic glaze before serving.

Nutritional Values per Serving: Calories: 236 kcal; Protein: 40 g; Carbohydrates: 4g; Dietary Fiber: 1g; Total Fat: 6g; Saturated Fat: 3g; Cholesterol: 15mg; Sodium: 100mg; Phosphorus: 100mg; Potassium: 100mg

Difficulty Rating: ☆

Tips: Use toothpicks if skewers are not available.

39. Hard-Boiled Eggs with Salt and Pepper

Servings: 2
Preparation time: 5 minutes
Cooking time: 10 minutes
Ingredients:

- 2 large eggs
- Salt and pepper to taste

Directions:

1. Place the eggs in a saucepan and cover with water.

2. Bring the water to a boil, then reduce the heat and simmer for 8-10 minutes.

3. Remove the eggs from the water and let them cool slightly.

4. Peel the eggs and sprinkle with salt and pepper.

Nutritional Values per Serving: Calories: 304 kcal; Protein: 24 g; Carbohydrates: 1g; Dietary Fiber: 0g; Total Fat: 5g; Saturated Fat: 2g; Cholesterol: 185mg; Sodium: 70mg; Phosphorus: 100mg; Potassium: 70mg

Difficulty Rating: ☆

Tips: Add a sprinkle of paprika for extra flavor.

40. Rice Cake with Avocado and Tomato

Servings: 1
Preparation time: 5 minutes
Ingredients:

- 1 rice cake
- 1/4 avocado, mashed
- 1 small tomato, sliced

Directions:

1. Spread the mashed avocado onto the rice cake.

2. Top with sliced tomato.

Nutritional Values per Serving: Calories: 63 kcal; Protein: 2.25 g; Carbohydrates: 15g; Dietary Fiber: 3g; Total Fat: 5g; Saturated Fat: 1g; Cholesterol: 0mg; Sodium: 10mg; Phosphorus: 80mg; Potassium: 200mg

Difficulty Rating: ☆

Tips: Sprinkle with a pinch of sea salt for added flavor.

CHAPTER 15: DIABETIC DIET DESSERTS

When it comes to desserts, individuals with diabetes may feel limited in their options. However, with the right knowledge and ingredients, it is possible to indulge in sweet treats without compromising blood sugar levels. This chapter aims to provide a variety of dessert options that are suitable for diabetics, catering to a wide range of individuals from high school education to college degrees.

The key focus of this chapter is to offer diabetic-friendly dessert recipes that are both delicious and nutritious. These recipes are carefully crafted to ensure they do not cause a spike in blood sugar levels. By using alternative sweeteners and incorporating ingredients that have a low glycemic index, these desserts can be enjoyed without guilt.

The chapter delves into the different types of diabetic-friendly desserts, including cakes, cookies, pies, and more. It provides detailed instructions on how to prepare these desserts, along with a list of recommended ingredients. Additionally, it offers tips on portion control and mindful eating to help individuals with diabetes maintain a balanced diet.

Furthermore, this chapter emphasizes the importance of incorporating ingredients that can help fight diabetes. It explores the use of whole grains, fruits, and nuts, which are known for their beneficial effects on blood sugar levels. By incorporating these ingredients into desserts, individuals with diabetes can enjoy a sweet treat while also promoting their overall health.

CHAPTER 16: AFFORDABLE DESSERTS RECIPES

41. Easy Berry Parfait

Servings: 4
Preparation time: 10 minutes
Cooking time: None
Ingredients:

• 2 cups of mixed berries (strawberries, blueberries, raspberries)
• 1 cup of plain Greek yogurt
• 2 tablespoons of sugar-free granola

Directions:

1. Wash and slice the berries.
2. In a glass or bowl, layer the berries and yogurt.
3. Repeat the layers until all the ingredients are used.
4. Top with sugar-free granola.

Nutritional Values per Serving: 473 kcal; Protein: 47 g; Carbohydrates: 18g; Dietary Fiber: 4g; Total Fat: 2g; Saturated Fat: 0g; Cholesterol: 0mg; Sodium: 20mg; Phosphorus: 80mg; Potassium: 200mg

Difficulty Rating: ☆ ☆

Tips: Use different types of berries or add a sprinkle of cinnamon for extra flavor.

Average cost: $3

42. Chocolate Avocado Mousse

Servings: 2
Preparation time: 15 minutes
Cooking time: None
Ingredients:

• 1 ripe avocado
• 2 tablespoons of unsweetened cocoa powder
• 2 tablespoons of sugar-free sweetener
• 1/2 teaspoon of vanilla extract
• 1/4 cup of unsweetened almond milk

Directions:

1. Scoop out the flesh of the avocado and place it in a blender or food processor.
2. Add the cocoa powder, sweetener, vanilla extract, and almond milk.
3. Blend until smooth and creamy.
4. Divide the mousse into serving dishes and refrigerate for at least 1 hour before serving.

Nutritional Values per Serving: Calories: 359 kcal; Protein: 7 g; Carbohydrates: 9g; Dietary Fiber: 6g; Total Fat: 15g; Saturated Fat: 2g; Cholesterol: 0mg; Sodium: 10mg; Phosphorus: 100mg; Potassium: 400mg

Difficulty Rating: ☆ ☆ ☆

Tips: Add a pinch of cinnamon or a sprinkle of chopped nuts on top for added crunch.

Average cost: $2.50

43. Apple Cinnamon Oatmeal Cookies

Servings: 12
Preparation time: 15 minutes
Cooking time: 15 minutes
Ingredients:

- 1 cup of rolled oats
- 1 cup of almond flour
- 1/4 cup of sugar-free sweetener
- 1 teaspoon of ground cinnamon
- 1/2 teaspoon of baking powder
- 1/4 teaspoon of salt
- 1/4 cup of unsweetened applesauce
- 2 tablespoons of melted coconut oil
- 1/2 teaspoon of vanilla extract

Directions:

1. Preheat the oven to 350°F (175°C), and line a baking sheet with parchment paper.
2. In a large bowl, combine the oats, almond flour, sweetener, cinnamon, baking powder, and salt.
3. In a separate bowl, whisk together the applesauce, coconut oil, and vanilla extract.
4. Add the wet ingredients to the dry ingredients and mix until well combined.
5. Drop spoonfuls of the dough onto the prepared baking sheet and flatten them with the back of a spoon.
6. Bake for 15 minutes or until golden brown.

Nutritional Values per Serving: Calories: 4146 kcal; Protein: 138 g; Carbohydrates: 8g; Dietary Fiber: 2g; Total Fat: 6g; Saturated Fat: 3g; Cholesterol: 0mg; Sodium: 60mg; Phosphorus: 50mg; Potassium: 100mg

Difficulty Rating: ☆ ☆ ☆
Tips: Add raisins or chopped nuts to the dough for extra texture.
Average cost: $3.50

44. Banana Ice Cream

Servings: 2
Preparation time: 5 minutes
Cooking time: None
Ingredients:

- 2 ripe bananas, sliced and frozen
- 2 tablespoons of unsweetened almond milk
- 1/2 teaspoon of vanilla extract

Directions:

1. Place the frozen banana slices, almond milk, and vanilla extract in a blender or food processor.
2. Blend until smooth and creamy, scraping down the sides as needed.
3. Serve immediately as soft-serve ice cream or transfer to a container and freeze for a firmer texture.

Nutritional Values per Serving: Calories: 434 kcal; Protein: 6.2 g; Carbohydrates: 30g; Dietary Fiber: 3g; Total Fat: 0g; Saturated Fat: 0g; Cholesterol: 0mg; Sodium: 0mg; Phosphorus: 40mg; Potassium: 400mg

Difficulty Rating: ☆
Tips: Add a tablespoon of unsweetened cocoa powder for a chocolatey twist.
Average cost: $1.50

45. Lemon Chia Seed Pudding

Servings: 4
Preparation time: 10 minutes
Cooking time: None
Ingredients:

- 1 cup of unsweetened almond milk
- 1/4 cup of chia seeds
- 2 tablespoons of sugar-free sweetener
- Zest and juice of 1 lemon

Directions:

1. In a bowl, whisk together the almond milk, chia seeds, sweetener, lemon zest, and lemon juice.

2. Let the mixture sit for 5 minutes, then whisk again to prevent clumping.

3. Cover the bowl and refrigerate for at least 2 hours or overnight.

4. Stir well before serving and divide into individual servings.

Nutritional Values per Serving: Calories: 318 kcal; Protein: 18 g; Carbohydrates: 8g; Dietary Fiber: 6g; Total Fat: 4g; Saturated Fat: 0g; Cholesterol: 0mg; Sodium: 20mg; Phosphorus: 100mg; Potassium: 100mg

Difficulty Rating: ☆ ☆

Tips: Add a teaspoon of vanilla extract or top with fresh berries for extra flavor.

Average cost: $2.50

46. Peanut Butter Energy Balls

Servings: 10
Preparation time: 10 minutes
Cooking time: None
Ingredients:

- 1 cup of rolled oats
- 1/2 cup of natural peanut butter
- 1/4 cup of sugar-free sweetener
- 2 tablespoons of ground flaxseed
- 2 tablespoons of unsweetened cocoa powder
- 1/4 cup of unsweetened almond milk

Directions:

1. In a large bowl, combine the oats, peanut butter, sweetener, flaxseed, cocoa powder, and almond milk.

2. Mix until well combined and the mixture holds together.

3. Roll the mixture into small balls, about 1 inch in diameter.

4. Place the energy balls on a baking sheet lined with parchment paper and refrigerate for at least 30 minutes before serving.

Nutritional Values per Serving: Calories: 2676 kcal; Protein: 120 g; Carbohydrates: 12g; Dietary Fiber: 4g; Total Fat: 8g; Saturated Fat: 1g; Cholesterol: 0mg; Sodium: 40mg; Phosphorus: 80mg; Potassium: 150mg

Difficulty Rating: ☆ ☆

Tips: Add chopped nuts or dried fruits for added texture and flavor.

Average cost: $3

47. Vanilla Chia Pudding

Servings: 4
Preparation time: 5 minutes
Cooking time: None
Ingredients:
• 1 cup of unsweetened almond milk
• 1/4 cup of chia seeds
• 2 tablespoons of sugar-free sweetener
• 1/2 teaspoon of vanilla extract
Directions:
1. In a bowl, whisk together the almond milk, chia seeds, sweetener, and vanilla extract.
2. Let the mixture sit for 5 minutes, then whisk again to prevent clumping.
3. Cover the bowl and refrigerate for at least 2 hours or overnight.
4. Stir well before serving and divide into individual servings.
Nutritional Values per Serving: Calories: 318 kcal; Protein: 18 g; Carbohydrates: 8g; Dietary Fiber: 6g; Total Fat: 4g; Saturated Fat: 0g; Cholesterol: 0mg; Sodium: 20mg; Phosphorus: 100mg; Potassium: 100mg
Difficulty Rating: ☆
Tips: Add a sprinkle of cinnamon or top with fresh fruit for extra flavor.
Average cost: $2.50

48. Baked Cinnamon Apple Chips

Servings: 4
Preparation time: 10 minutes
Cooking time: 2 hours
Ingredients:
• 2 apples, cored and thinly sliced
• 1 teaspoon of ground cinnamon
• 1/2 teaspoon of sugar-free sweetener
Directions:
1. Preheat the oven to 200°F (95°C) and line a baking sheet with parchment paper.
2. In a bowl, toss the apple slices with cinnamon and sweetener until coated.
3. Arrange the apple slices in a single layer on the prepared baking sheet.
4. Bake for 2 hours or until the chips are crisp, flipping them halfway through.
Nutritional Values per Serving: Calories: 418 kcal; Protein: 2.4 g; Carbohydrates: 15g; Dietary Fiber: 4g; Total Fat: 0g; Saturated Fat: 0g; Cholesterol: 0mg; Sodium: 0mg; Phosphorus: 20mg; Potassium: 100mg
Difficulty Rating: ☆ ☆
Tips: Sprinkle with a pinch of nutmeg or drizzle with melted dark chocolate for a treat.
Average cost: $2

49. Pumpkin Spice Muffins

Servings: 12
Preparation time: 15 minutes
Cooking time: 20 minutes
Ingredients:

- 1 cup of almond flour
- 1/2 cup of coconut flour
- 1/4 cup of sugar-free sweetener
- 1 teaspoon of baking powder
- 1/2 teaspoon of baking soda
- 1/2 teaspoon of ground cinnamon
- 1/4 teaspoon of ground nutmeg
- 1/4 teaspoon of ground ginger
- 1/4 teaspoon of salt
- 1 cup of canned pumpkin puree
- 1/4 cup of unsweetened almond milk
- 2 tablespoons of melted coconut oil
- 2 large eggs

Directions:

1. Preheat the oven to 350°F (175°C) and line a muffin tin with paper liners.

2. In a large bowl, whisk together the almond flour, coconut flour, sweetener, baking powder, baking soda, cinnamon, nutmeg, ginger, and salt.

3. In a separate bowl, whisk together the pumpkin puree, almond milk, coconut oil, and eggs.

4. Add the wet ingredients to the dry ingredients and mix until just combined.

5. Divide the batter evenly among the muffin cups.

6. Bake for 20 minutes or until a toothpick inserted into the center comes out clean.

Nutritional Values per Serving: 449 kcal; Protein: 156 g; Carbohydrates: 8g; Dietary Fiber: 4g; Total Fat: 10g; Saturated Fat: 5g; Cholesterol: 35mg; Sodium: 180mg; Phosphorus: 100mg; Potassium: 150mg

Difficulty Rating: ☆ ☆ ☆

Tips: Add chopped walnuts or raisins to the batter for added texture and flavor.

Average cost: $4

50. Greek Yogurt Bark

Servings: 8
Preparation time: 10 minutes
Cooking time: 2 hours
Ingredients:

- 2 cups of plain Greek yogurt
- 2 tablespoons of sugar-free sweetener
- 1/2 teaspoon of vanilla extract
- 1/4 cup of unsweetened shredded coconut
- 1/4 cup of chopped nuts (almonds, walnuts, or pistachios)
- 1/4 cup of sugar-free dark chocolate chips

Directions:

1. In a bowl, mix together the Greek yogurt, sweetener, and vanilla extract.

2. Line a baking sheet with parchment paper and spread the yogurt mixture evenly.

3. Sprinkle the shredded coconut, chopped nuts, and dark chocolate chips over the yogurt.

4. Freeze for at least 2 hours or until firm.

5. Break the bark into pieces and serve immediately.

Nutritional Values per Serving: 364 kcal; Protein: 200 g; Carbohydrates: 6g; Dietary Fiber: 2g; Total Fat: 8g; Saturated Fat: 4g; Cholesterol: 0mg; Sodium: 20mg; Phosphorus: 80mg; Potassium: 200mg

Difficulty Rating: ☆ ☆

Tips: Add dried fruit or a sprinkle of cinnamon for extra flavor and texture.

Average cost: $3.50

CHAPTER 17: CONVERSION CHART

Volume Equivalents (Liquid)

US Standard	US Standard (ounces)	Metric (approximate)
2 tablespoons	1 fl. oz.	30 mL
¼ cup	2 fl. oz.	60 mL
½ cup	4 fl. oz.	120 mL
1 cup	8 fl. oz.	240 mL
1½ cups	12 fl. oz.	355 mL
2 cups or 1 pint	16 fl. oz.	475 mL
4 cups or 1 quart	32 fl. oz.	1 L
1 gallon	128 fl. oz.	4 L

Volume Equivalents (Dry)

US Standard	Metric (approximate)
⅛ teaspoon	0.5 mL
¼ teaspoon	1 mL
½ teaspoon	2 mL
¾ teaspoon	4 mL
1 teaspoon	5 mL
1 tablespoon	15 mL
¼ cup	59 mL
⅓ cup	79 mL
½ cup	118 mL

⅔ cup	156 mL
¾ cup	177 mL
1 cup	235 mL
2 cups or 1 pint	475 mL
3 cups	700 mL
4 cups or 1 quart	1 L

Oven Temperatures

Fahrenheit (F)	Celsius (C) (approximate)
250 deg. F	120°C
300 deg. F	150°C
325 deg. F	165°C
350 deg. F	180°C
375 deg. F	190°C
400 deg. F	200°C
425 deg. F	220°C
450 deg. F	230°C

Weight Equivalents

US Standard	Metric (approximate)
1 tablespoon	15 g
½ ounce	15 g
1 ounce	30 g
2 ounces	60 g

4 ounces	115 g
8 ounces	225 g
12 ounces	340 g
16 ounces or 1 pound	455 g

INDEX

Made in the USA
Coppell, TX
22 July 2024

35057735R00037